A word of welcome from TIM McKAY . . .

WHEN I compiled my first crossword for the Daily Express back in the early 'Fifties, I gave no thought to the day when I would be nearing by ten thousandth — but it's coming close to hand, and this book of puzzles is the tenth I have produced for the Black Glass palace of Fleet Street. With this size of book I am able to give you a bigger variety of puzzles, and I hope to publish four or five of this new series every year. So whatever your tastes are in crosswords, you should get something to suit you in each issue.

CONTENTS

The cover design is by DAVID EDGELL whose wit enlivens many Daily Express features. The portrait of TIM McKAY on the back cover is by Cotswold artist Kay Arnott, and it was photographed by Reg Lancaster.
PUBLISHED BY EXPRESS NEWSPAPERS LTD. ©1980
Printed by J. H. Lake & Co. Ltd., The Falmouth Packet, Ponsharden, Falmouth, Cornwall.

ISBN 0 85079 105   TMPB1

Personality Codewords

These have been called "the cleverest crosswords yet". The idea is that you identify the popular singer in the photograph, put his first name in the marked squares. The numbers there will help you to fill in other squares throughout the grid with the same letters. Soon you will be able to form new words and by trial and error you will solve the whole puzzle . . . all from a three-letter clue. Solution at the end of the book.

Personality Codewords 1.

C1	C2	C3	C4	C5	C6	C7	C8	C9	C10	C11	C12	C13	C14	C15
10	9	8	7	11	6	5		12	5	6	15	1	13	14
7		7		1	6		6		3			5		9
14	7	15	6	5		16	6	11	17	3	5	7	8	9
6		9		1		1		9		1		15		2
18	9	14	6	2	7	13	10	3		11	19	9	6	4
9		3				14				7				9
3	4	7	12	12		7	11	9	5	6	2	8	9	14
		1		6		4		3				4	9	
11	1	2	8	7	10	9	2	4		9	6	4	9	2
6				4				14				14		13
20	9	14	11	19		8	7	6	20	19	14	6	18	10
6		13		5		14		2		1		11		16
16	6	2	4	9	14	7	2	18		10	9	4	14	9
5		7		3		9		9		9		1		14
9	2	11	6	3	9	8		8	9	3	9	14	4	3

Personality Codewords

The second Personality is a girl singer overflowing with bezazz. Identify her picture, put her first name in the marked squares of the crossword. To complete the puzzle you transfer the letters of her name to similarly-marked squares throughout the grid. Words soon show up and soon you can cross off most of the alphabet.

Personality Codewords 2.

11	9	10	9	11	8	9		11	9	12	7	6	13	9
9		6		9		1		4		11		7		15
13	3	7	7	6		12	11	4	10	3	14	3	15	16
9		19		13		7		17		15		10		4
3	15	6	12	17	15	9	8	8		13	18	9	9	11
12		20				17				3				16
17	19	7	3	12		3	15	13	9	12	17	3	10	9
		9		9		10		6		6		15		
11	9	8	19	11	16	9	15	17		7	3	8	17	8
9				8				6				17		19
12	6	17	3	4		5	4	7	7	4	2	3	15	16
11		9		15		11		4		7		16		16
9	1	12	9	15	14	3	15	16		3	15	6	15	9
8		3		9		6		19		10		17		8
8	6	14	14	7	9	11		9	10	9	11	9	8	17

3

Personality Codewords

This puzzle features a television man who puts contestants through the most gruelling tasks in a race for a shower of coffee pots, tea-sets and non-stick frying pans. Write his first name in the marked squares, then transfer the letters to similarly marked squares elsewhere. Dotted lines indicate hyphens or linked words. You will find that words build up in an astonishing fashion. But take care. A slip can result in a lot of words spelled like a sneeze.

Personality Codewords 3.

10	9	8	12	6	7	6	7	5		5	4	3	12	12
	14		9		2		6				7		8	
13	2	7	7	6	13	4	6	14		13	2	8	2	11
	8		6		16		5		10		2		1	
3	5	10	9	13		5	4	7	9	10	10	6	7	5
			7				3		11				15	
5	4	2	2	10		2	15	5	4	6	4	7	9	13
	7		11		3		8		5		6		11	
11	1	7	5	6	17	3	9	14		9	7	9	5	18
	11				2		5				7			
2	11	5	8	3	1	19	18	4		8	3	7	7	20
	9		2		7		17		16		10		6	
7	2	4	2	7		12	6	17	9	11	9	5	4	5
	11		5				11		8		11		9	
1	5	18	6	7		5	4	3	4	6	5	17	6	11

4

Personality Codewords

Identify the man in the photograph . . . you may have seen him entertaining young people with his songs and drawings on television. Jot down his first name in the marked space, then match up the letters there with similar-numbered squares in the grid. Words appear like magic and new letters add new words. You can solve all the words from the original four of our Personality's first name.

Personality Codewords 4.

5	6	10	10	7	9	1		10	6	13	11	9	14	4
8		9		14		3		9		17		21		5
7	15	16	17	9		8	7	12	18	14	15	3	10	9
10		9		15		12		3		9		15		9
10	6	2	19		4	2	20	2	20		19	7	4	14
9				7		9		9		4		8		9
1	3	10	14	4		1	9	1	17	13	14	7	6	8
		9		2			12			3		8		
18	6	14	14	9	8	14	6	14		10	3	12	9	4
6		3		4		10		10		19				9
10	17	7	8		19	7	23	9	10		4	6	2	1
10		8		19		22		4		9		17		17
6	23	9	10	10	17	2	9	4		15	3	12	7	13
10		10		9		9		9		7		18		9
4	17	4	22	9	13	14		4	22	10	7	14	9	4

Personality Codewords

PERSONALITY No. 5 is a film star with a famous smile and a reputation that he wears like a halo. Put his first name in the circled squares, then extend the letters to all the similar-numbered squares as in the previous puzzles. An experienced puzzler should take 20 minutes to 30 minutes over the puzzle. A beginner may take an hour.

Personality Codewords 5.

9	4	10	7	6	5	11	4	9		12	13	4	7	14
4		2		5		7		4		7		9		4
3	5	15	16	16		10	4	10	2	9	7	5	11	7
19		5		1		2		2		9		6		
2	15	14	1	7	17	3		18	6	2	1	4	14	3
5		7		10		4		4		14				6
3	5	6	18	4	1	1	4	9	3		8	2	5	11
6		5		11					3		18			4
8	7	3	13		3	19	6	9	6	14	1	4	3	3
1			12		1		4		7		9			7
4	11	15	12	7	14	4		19	7	9	12	13	4	11
		5		9		7		2		20		7		11
3	15	9	9	4	5	11	4	9		7	5	5	15	1
6		6		4		4		14		21		20		4
9	2	20	4	9		11	6	3	19	4	5	3	4	3

6

Personality Codewords

A famous statesman for this one. Maybe not his nation's primest example, but one who had to face up perhaps to more problems than most. Print his surname in the marked squares and then match up the letters there with similar-numbered squares throughout the grid. No letter has more than one number. Solution at the end of the book.

Personality Codewords 6.

7	2	6	8	10	9	11	12		1	2	15	8	6	9
2		2		9		9				16		6		14
11	8	4	8	20	2	4	5		1	2	3	13	5	15
8		18		20		4		2		4		5		1
1	18	3	3	22	1	9	7	14		17	8	6	12	18
5		5			2			11	5	5		4		3
			17	18	7	2	6	5		4	17	9	15	5
1		3		6		16		15		8		3		12
9	16	5	3	2		2	4	4	2	1	19			
18		20		15	2	1			15			1		10
1	3	18	15	17		17	9	3	15	5	17	2	8	3
17		11		2		5		5		11		3		9
2	11	2	3	7	15		16	5	12	5	15	4	2	11
6		4		5			11			1		5		8
4	21	5	5	12	22		5	15	9	4	5	3	8	1

7

Personality Codewords

A film star and a great beauty. It's her surname that must be put in the marked squares. When you have completed the task of transferring the letters of the name to similar-numbered squares in the grid, you will find a tantalising set of choices. Pick the right ones and you are home and dry. Solution at the end of the book.

Personality Codewords 7.

5	4	3	4	10	11	5		12	4	13	14	2	12	5
4		6		13		11		6		6		9		2
10	2	13	15	6		4	16	12	6	17	4	13	4	7
6		4		17		2		18		5		15		7
8	6	8	4		5	16	2	3	3		12	2	3	3
7			9		4		2		14		18		4
5	12	4	4	7		7	4	13	13	9	8	15	4	13
		8		4			20			8		4	
13	4	7	14	2	8	7	4	7		15	18	5	11	19
4		4		3		4		13		4			4
12	4	2	13		5	12	9	4	7		1	4	11	2
4		13		20		13		5		2		3		13
8	6	9	5	4	3	4	5	5		8	19	3	6	8
11		8		11		5		4		8		4		4
5	9	15	8	6	13	5		7	13	2	9	8	4	7

Codewords

A CODEWORD is a crossword puzzle without a clue
. . . or more properly, without normal clues. The puzzle on this page, like those on the three following pages, has only one clue of a three letter word, printed in it. Each letter of the clue has a number and if you transfer the letter to every other square in the grid with that number you can build up a lot of other words. Watch out though. You may worry why things are not working out and at last trace it back to your own carelessness in putting down a word like Needful instead of Heedful! Expert crossword solvers should be able to complete the Codeword in 30 minutes or less, but beginners may take up to an hour.

Codewords 1.

C1	C2	C3	C4	C5	C6	C7	C8	C9	C10	C11	C12	C13	C14	C15
11	9	10	8	7	8	12	■	7	6	9	13	14	10	5
4	■	8	■	9	■	4	9	■	13	■	10	■	■	20
6	9	15	4	16	S	U (3)	P (13)	11	5	6	17	8	3	5
4	■	11	■	18	■	3	■	5	■	3	■	3	■	10
11	6	8	17	4	7	5	5	6	■	5	10	3	8	5
5	■	19	■	■	■	6	■	■	■	10	■	■	■	7
7	4	8	10	3	■	9	14	10	8	17	8	9	13	3
■	■	7	■	22	■	10	■	8	■	5	■	21	■	■
21	10	20	11	4	11	5	6	3	■	3	8	21	7	3
5	■	■	■	6	■	■	■	7	■	■	■	5	■	4
3	2	8	15	11	■	12	22	5	1	13	5	6	5	19
7	■	16	■	5	■	6	■	16	■	16	■	8	■	8
5	16	19	4	16	18	5	6	3	■	21	13	16	19	3
6	■	8	■	5	■	4	■••••	8	■	5	■	18	■	7
3	7	4	6	19	9	15	■	16	13	19	8	3	7	3

Codewords

SOME solvers find it helps to write down the alphabet and check each letter with the number when it is proved correct.

Codewords 2.

16	1	10	10	11	9	8	7	12	■	1	13	13	6	5
■	14	■	6	■	8	■	19	■	■	■	5	■	5	■
10	4	2	2	4	9	15	4	17	■	17	6	5	5	12
■	2	■	2	■	4	••••	4	■	14	■	8	■	1	■
17	4 (L)	5 (A)	6 (Y)	12	■	8	9	7	4	15	17	8	7	12
■	■	■	16	■	■	18	■	6	■	■	■	■	10	■
2	20	6	17	4	■	16	1	9	18	4	9	2	4	17
■	6	■	4	■	2	■	13	■	12	■	6	■	9	■
4	17	6	18	8	16	6	7	4	■	14	17	11	7	4
■	6	■	■	■	4	■	19	■	■	■	16	■	■	■
2	16	6	3	4	9	15	4	17	■	21	1	17	2	4
■	19	■	4	■	7	••••	5	■	7	■	7	■	8	■
16	11	17	17	12	■	16	8	3	8	5	8	2	4	18
■	7	■	2	■	■	■	9	■	4	■	16	■	15	■
2	4	3	4	17	■	17	4	13	17	4	2	19	4	18

Codewords

DOTTED lines indicate hyphens or linked words.

You're in good company with Tim McKay.

Codewords 3.

3	2	1	9	8	7	6	▓	7	R₁	A	P₅	10	10	9	3
1	▓	2	▓	13	▓	10		13	▓	16	▓	15	▓		9
9	5	11	9	1	▓	15	13	14	1	2	8	5	7	▓	9
5	▓	2	▓	5	▓	13	▓	9	▓	12	▓	7	▓		12
12	9	3	2	7	5	7	9	3	▓	5	15	2	14	2	
9	▓		▓	4	▓	7	▓		▓	15	▓	7	▓		16
3	9	7	9	1	11	9	16	7	▓	6	7	13	16		11
▓	▓	9	▓	▓	▓	1	▓	1	▓	▓	▓	3	▓	▓	▓
10	2	15	15	6	▓	6	7	5	7	9	12	9	16		7
4	▓	9	▓	9	▓			16	▓	15	▓		▓		4
15	9	10	9	1	▓	9	5	6	7	9	1	9	11		11
9	▓	18	▓	12	▓	17	▓	8	▓	12	▓	5	▓		11
8	18	4	8	4	15	5	7	9	▓	9	5	6	9		15
5	▓	16	▓	16	▓	12	▓	16	▓	16	▓	9	▓		9
7	1	9	6	6	9	6	▓	3	9	7	9	6	7		6

11

Codewords

SOLUTIONS are at the end of the book.

> Once you're in the swing it's easy.

Codewords 4.

								T	A	N				
4	3	2	10	9	2	8	7	2	6	4	5	9	4	11
13	▓	3	▓	3	▓	2	▓	11	▓	13	▓	▓		15
2	▓	1	6	5	9	6	2	3	1	7	▓			4
14	3	14	12	▓	3	▓	11	▓	11	▓	2	1	3	2
1	▓	3		22	▓	14	▓	14	▓	5	▓	15	▓	18
6	4	4	13	18	6	1	▓	3	21	15	1	7	15	15
14	▓	2	▓	3	▓	13	1	4	▓	9	▓	3	▓	19
12	4	9	2	2	15	5	▓	9	4	20	6	4	2	6
15	▓	4	▓	2	▓	15	18	20	▓	9	▓	6	▓	4
1	3	13	2	15	1	7	▓	15	2	15	1	4	6	18
7	▓	15	▓	1	▓	2	▓	1	▓	5	▓	14	▓	9
13	4	5	3	▓	20	▓	9	▓	5	▓	19	15	6	4
9	▓	▓	11	1	6	4	5	7	9	1	15	▓	▓	15
2	▓	▓	1	▓	2	▓	15	▓	7	▓	4	▓	▓	7
15	16	17	15	4	7	15	6	14	14	3	13	4	2	7

Small Crosswords

The puzzles that bring all the "bless-you" letters to Tim McKay. "I think I must have more friends than anyone in London," he says. "I could keep twenty five secretaries busy answering all my letters."

Small Crosswords 1.

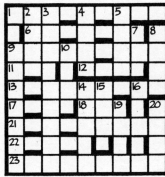

Across

1. Street trader. (6-3)
6. Portable home. (7)
9. Tough hide. (5, 4)
11. Fowl. (3)
12. Ooze. (4)

13. Coarse material. (9)
17. Competent. (4)
18. Mien. (3)
21. Survey the scene. (4, 5)
22. Cornish city. (5)
23. Indicator. (9)

Down

1. Blasts hat (anag). (4-5)
2. Soreness. (4)
3. Weather feature. (9)
4. Trees. (4)
5. Cook. (4)
7. Pinch. (3)
8. Measure, (4)
10. Fuel. (4)
14. Christmas song. (5)
15. Z o o a nimal. (4)
16. S m all portion. (5)
19. Part of a ladder. (4)
20. E n t - rance to a mine. (4)

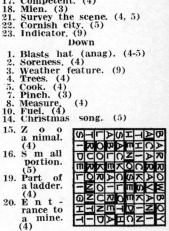

Small Crosswords 2.

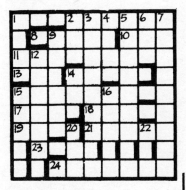

1. Cinema films. (3, 6)
8. Move gracefully on ice. (5)
10. Miss West. (3)
11. Generous soul. (4, 5)
13. Girl's name. (3)
14. Rough material for suits. (5)
15. She appears on magazines. (5, 4)

17. Basement. (4)
18. Flinch (5)
19. Loving touch (4)
21. Covered with greenery. (5)
23. Optics. (4)
24. Light automatic weapon. (4, 3)

Down

1. Capture. (4)
2. Unbalanced. (3)
3. I see worth (anag.). (9)
4. Change direction. (4)
5. Visualising. (9)
6. Highly developed in the case of guard dogs. (3)
7. Made to feel at home. (7, 2)
9. Villains. (6)
12. Piano keys. (7)
14. North on Britain's E a s t. (3)
15. B a k e d for tea. (5)
16. Donated. (5)
20. S o l idi- fied. (3)
22. L a r g e b i r d. (3)

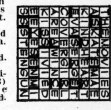

Small Crosswords

Start your day with Tim McKay in the Daily Express.

Small Crosswords 3.

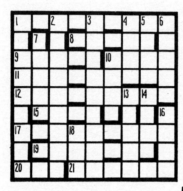

Across

1. A halfpenny, perhaps. (5, 4)
8. Plays boisterously. (5)
9. Milk shop. (5)
10. Retained. (4)
11. Neat diner (anag.). (9)
12. Chasing and about to overtake. (2, 4, 3)

15. Sediment. (4)
17. Belief about a person's guilt. (9)
19. Covered with linen. (7)
20. Cathedral city. (3)
21. Stage remarks. (6)

Down

1. Not the main topic. (4, 5)
2. Arousing a certain amount of distrust. (1, 3, 5)
3. Allegiances. (9)
4. Frank. (4)
5. Land surrounded by water. (4)
6. Toyland character. (5)
7. Notices of intended marriage. (5)
10. Mound. (4)
13. Shouted. (5)
14. Measure of land. (4)
16. Burden. (4)
18. Vegetable. (3)

Small Crosswords 4.

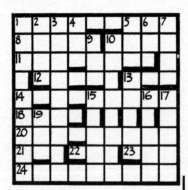

Across

1. Sales assistants. (4-5)
8. Mates. (5)
10. Manner of walking. (4)
11. Zoo animal. (8)
12. Salvers. (5)
13. Taste. (3)
14. Famous plane. (5, 4)

18. Annoy. (4)
20. Art of reciting. (9)
21. Stitch. (3)
22. Consumed. (3)
23. Timed. (3)
24. Freedom from deceit. (9)

Down

1. Shown by a person of a lovable nature. (9)
2. Sword-handle. (4)
3. Too tall for his age. (9)
4. Liveliness. (3)
5. Hurried. (3)
6. Applied flame. (3)
7. Halt. (4)
9. Reticent. (3)
10. Measuring device used in many homes. (3-5)
13. Stable. (5)
15. Directions for journey. (5)
16. Fish. (5)
17. Sweet substance. (5)
19. Beer. (3)

Small Crosswords

Small Crosswords 5.

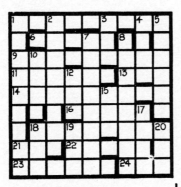

16. Spirit. (5)
13. Serves food. (6, 2)
21. Age. (3)
22. Part of a target. (5)
23. Is mean about things. (6)
24. Heavens. (3)

Down
1. For the mail. (4-3)
2. Wild animal pelt. (4, 4)
3. Fabulous bird. (3)
4. Girl's name. (4)
5. Contrivance. (6)
7. Temporary building on the shore. (5, 3)
8. Worries. (8)
10. Garment. (4)
12. C r a f t. (3)
15. Delicacy on toast. (3)
18. P o i nt. (3)
19. C h i l d. (3)
20. H a n d o u t m o ney. (3)

Across
1. Petty thieving. (9)
6. Empty space. (5)
9. Cords race (anag.). (9)
11. Pacific islander. (6)
13. Torn cloth. (3)
14. On which a pay structure is built. (5, 4)

Small Crosswords 6.

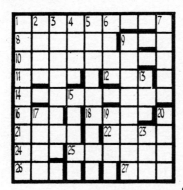

21. Ditch. (4)
22. Ascend. (4)
24. Age. (3)
24. Sixpence. (6)
26. May describe a popular blue. (3)
27. Horse. (3)

Down
1. Spend your time at golf or tennis. (4, 5)
2. Narrow thoroughfare. (4)
3. Church of England member. (8)
4. Image. (4)
5. Scandinavian. (9)
6. Fill overfull. (4)
7. Stakes in some card games. (5)
9. Frowning in ill-tempered way. (8)
13. F r i e nd. (3)
15. S o n g. (5)
17. Swindle. (4)
19. V a s e- s h a ped containers. (4)
20. L a k e. (4)
23. D e scry. (3)

Across
1. A good one is what many housewives aspire to be. (5, 4)
8. Victorian poet. (6)
9. Go winter-sporting. (3)
10. Long-haired pet. (6, 3)
11. Cry aloud. (4)
12. Cleaner. (3)
14. Die, Galway (anag.). (5, 4)
16. Part of a circle. (3)
18. Seabird. (4)

Small Crosswords

Small Crosswords 7.

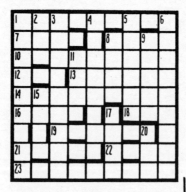

12. Cheese. (4)
14. Property dealer (4-5)
18. State rule. (3)
20. Entertaining. (7)
21. Scattered water. (8)
22. Type of conifer. (6, 3)

Down

1. Complete wreck. (5, 4)
2. Hadrian built one in the North of England. (5, 4)
3. Snug. (4)
4. Revile unendingly. (4, 5)
5. Carpenter's tool. (3)
6. Blood. (4)
7. Girl's name. (4)
9. French river. (5)
13. Deliverance from pain. (6)
15. Weakly-lit. (3)
16. Stream copiously. (4)
17. Asiatic feline. (5)
19. Mountain. (3)

Across

1. Och, strong (Anag.). (5-4)
7. Bird noise. (3)
8. Consumes. (4)
10. American boy hero of story. (3, 6)
11. Beam. (3)

Small Crosswords 8.

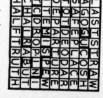

16. One of a list. (4)
18. Seat in church. (3)
19. Look us up any time. (4, 2)
21. Seat. (5)
22. Adjoin. (4)
23. It's partly correct. (4-5)

Down

1. For persistent defenders. (4, 5)
2. Eastern title. (3)
3. For quiet passages. (4, 5)
4. More excellent. (8)
5. Warning to some motorists. (4, 2)
6. Hew, wither (anag.). (9)
8. Cream is made to. in some parts of the country. (4)
9. Frighten. (5)
11. One kind of Continental cheese. (4)
15. Eat away with acids. (4)
17. Box. (4)
20. Filbert, perhaps. (3)

Across

1. With which breaking point is reached. (4, 5)
7. Full of vitality. (4)
8. Weapon. (4)
10. For security. (4, 5)
12. Short drink. (3)
13. Kind of tree. (6)
14. Tear prude (anag.). (9)

Small Crosswords

Small Crosswords 9.

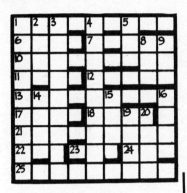

Across
1. Old pun. (5, 4)
6. Water movement. (4)
7. Grass cutter. (5)
10. Courts of Justice. (3, 6)
11. Old emperor. (4)
12. Peer. (5)
13. Eminence. (9)
17. Price. (4)   18. Labels. (4)
21. Stubborn. (9)
22. Shelter. (3)
23. Marsh. (3)
24. Youngster. (3)
25. Break contact. (9)

Down
1. Frigid. (5-4)
2. Top hat. (4)   3. Talks. (9)
4. Into a name (anag.). (9)
5. Night bird (3)
8. Slippery fish. (3)
9. Grain. (3)
14. Part of the ear. (4)
15. Flavour (4)
16. Necessity. (4)
19. Fete. (4)
20. Deer. (4)

Small Crosswords 10.

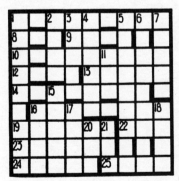

Across
1. Forceful words with which playwright ends a scene. (5-4)
8. Spanish river. (3)
9. Shower. (4)
10. Money earning interest. (2, 7)
12. Irish dish ? 4)
13. Use leverage. (5)
14. Make weak. (8)
16. Miserly action. (8)
19. For lubrication work. (6)
22. At this moment. (3)
23. Girl's name. (6)
24. Repairs. (5)
25. Threads interwoven with warp. (4)

Down
1. More popes (anag.). (5, 4)
2. Knot. (4)
3. Famous junction. (5)
4. Occur. (6)
5. Without a word. (2, 7)
6. They are heard from behind the scenes. (6, 3)
7. Consumed. (5)
11. Globe. (3)
15. Criminal. (5)
16. Distance. (4)
17. Bitter substance. (4)
18. Kill that fly. (4)
20. Foolish fellow. (3)
21. Novel. (3)

Small Crosswords

Small Crosswords 11.

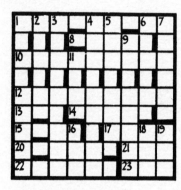

Across
1. Frog's woad (anag.). (4, 2, 3)
8. Nautical speed. (5)
10. Financial scheme. (4, 5)
12. For waste paper. (6, 3)
13. Cathedral city. (3)
14. Grow larger. (5)
15. Weapons. (4)
17. Stitched. (4)
20. Washes. (6)
21. Small deer. (3)
22. Offer to trade. (6)
23. Provide poem with music. (3)

Down
1. Like Morecambe and Wise. (6, 3)
2. This payment is made at once. (2, 4)
3. The criminals involved. (6, 3)
4. Like the moon late in its time. (2, 3, 4)
5. Stronghold. (8)
6. Attack. (6)
7. Part of the eye. (6)
9. Circus experts. (8)
11. Tiny children. (4)
16. Dismal. (3)
18. Sorrow. (3)
19. Mesh. (3)

Small Crosswords 12.

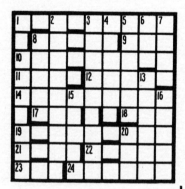

Across
1. He is just the chap to win a gold for Britain. (5, 4)
8. Something to go with your afternoon tea. (5)
9. Poem, perhaps. (3)
10. Naked, or dateless. (7, 2)
11. Plum, perhaps. (4)
12. Battle. (5)
14. Given a coat of hard paint. (9)
17. Expire. (3)
18. Given by those who pay attention. (3)
19. Spread light. (9)
21. Amounting to nothing. (4)
22. Kind of plums. (5)
23. Happy. (3)
24. Cuts. (6)

Down
1. Offering by way of payment. (9)
2. Perform duties with justice. (3, 6)
3. Sharp blade. (5-4)
4. Deterioration of old age. (6)
5. Short pin through loop, with link to keep it in place. (6)
6. Fuss. (3)
7. Payment for accommodation. (4)
8. Noise. (5)
13. Warmer. (6)
15. Food. (5)
16. Frock. (5)
20. The times. (3)

18

Small Crosswords

Small Crosswords 13.

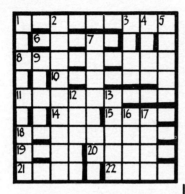

Across
1. This kind of chase may be a hoax. (4, 5)
6. Loop. (5)
8. Accumulation of goods. (5-4)
10. Woollen garment maker. (7)
11. Facsimile. (5, 4)
14. Auction item. (3)
15. Friend. (4)
18. Idea if C.I.D. get in a mix up. (9)
19. Part of the church sounds villainous. (4)
20. Transmits. (5)
21. Action. (4)
22. Saturate. (4)

Down
1. Steal wand (anag.). (5, 4)
2. Jump to it! (4, 5)
3. Leave out. (4)
4. Only. (4)
5. Abrasive. (5)
7. Excessively lively. (8)
9. Poisonous. (5)
12. Written in morse, for instance. (5)
13. Refreshment houses. (5)
16. Floor covering. (4)
17. She was wooed by a swan. (4)

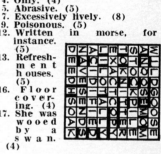

Small Crosswords 14.

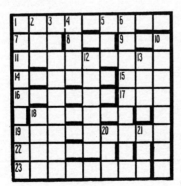

Across
1. Repaired. (7, 2)
7. Time past. (3)
8. Zoo animal. (3)
9. Consume. (3)
11. Stop press. (4, 5)
14. Temper. (6)
15. Salmon river. (3)
16. Fine cloth. (6)
17. Marry. (3)
18. Traveller. (6)
19. Use at hobo (anag.). (5-4)
22. Tell confidently. (6)
23. African river. (3, 5)

Down
1. Straw headgear. (6, 3)
2. Number of years. (3)
3. One in a crowded street, perhaps. (4, 5)
4. Suit for trial. (4)
5. Fish. (3)
6. Opposite of quite right. (4, 5)
10. Noted for their canals and land reclamation schemes. (5, 5)
12. More lovely. (6)
13. Ooze. (4)
18. Nonsense. (4)
20. Scottish mountain. (3)
21. Difficulty. (3)

Small Crosswords

Small Crosswords 15.

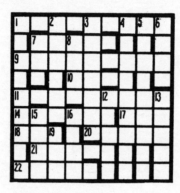

Across
1. Part of Hampshire. (3, 6)
7. Foyer. (5)
9. Feminine fashion. (4-5)
10. Canvas shelter. (4)
11. Steep fall. (5, 4)
14. Do well. (6). 17. Anger. (3)

18. Scots town. (3)
20. He made famous collection of marble statues. (5)
21. Famous Australian singer. (5)
22. Finished. (5)

Down
1. Without error. (2, 7)
2. Marvel. (6)
3. Perceive. (7)
4. The actor goes off, you are quite correct. (4, 5)
5. To do with tailoring. (9)
6. Dancer's short skirt. (4)
7. Edge. (3)
8. Angler's catch. (4)
12. W a i t. (5)
13. S m a l l c o i n. (5)
15. R e l i- g i o u s s o n g. (4)
16. L a z y. (4)
19. Colour. (3)

Small Crosswords 16.

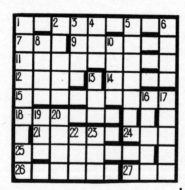

Across
1. Start your labours. (5, 4)
7. Girl's name. (3)
9. Apply attractive markings. (6)
11. Char. (5, 4)
12. Coal pit. (4)
14. Regiment. (4)
15. Necessary. (9)

18. Short time. (6)
21. Loop. (5) 24. Fish. (3)
25. In a dependable fashion. (8)
26. Gives up. (6)
27. Tree. (3)

Down
1. Amnesia. (3, 6)
2. Profits. (5)
3. Workshy. (4)
4. Old negative. (3)
5. Opportunity. (7)
6. Retained. (4)
8. Platform. (4)
10. Sound of a breakdown ! (4)
13. Tavern. (3)
16. The matches are not played at home. (5)
17. H e a v y s i d e- w a y s :n otion. (5)
19. S i ngle- ton. (3)
20. D,i gger. (4)
22. L u b r i- cate. (3)
23. D i smal. (3)

Small Crosswords

Small Crosswords 17.

14. Ocean. (3)
15. Nobody. (9)
19. Musical instruments. (6)
20. Expert musicians. (9)
23. Dear to any editor. (6)
24. Meadow. (3)
25. Joining up. (9)

Down

1. Cost of journey. (5, 4)
2. Peel. (4)
3. For the most part. (2, 7)
4. Number of years. (3)
5. Lie about. (4)
6. Dried fruit. (6)
7. Tavern. (3)
9. Upbraid. (4)
12. Declares. (4)
16. Numbers. (5)
17. Ripped. (4)
18. Small bird. (4)
19. Cushion. (3)
21. Biblical character. (3)
22. Droop. (3)

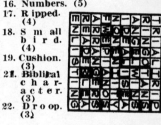

Across

1. Experimental journey. (5, 4)
8. Once a noted drummer. (5)
9. Sunburns. (4)
10. Backer for the show. (5)
11. Defeats the others. (4)
13. Best possible. (5)

Small Crosswords 18.

16. Generosity. (4, 5)
18. Top. (3)   19. Wet. (6)
21. Part of the services. (2, 7)
24. Near the Himalayas. (5)
25. Important bone. (4)
26. Country beginning. (5, 4)

Down

1. Complete lack of pretence. (2, 7)
2. Biblical character. (3)
3. Agitated. (7, 2)
4. Antique. (3)
5. South American city. (3)
6. Sipped. (6)   9. Enemy. (3)
10. Hard rubber. (6)
12. Wrong. (3)
14. Backbone. (5)
15. Make a noise like a bee. (3)
17. Containers. (5)
20. Equestrian game. (4)
22. Dressed pelts. (3)
23. Rug. (3)

Across

1. Wooded area. (3, 6)
7. Timber. (3)
8. Vitality. (4)
11. Conifers. (4)
13. Portals. (5)
14. Cavort. (4)
15. Warmth. (4)

Small Crosswords

Small Crosswords 19.

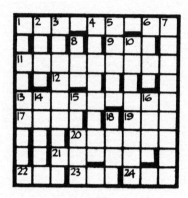

17. Grow weary. (4)
19. Public transport. (3)
20. Night-birds. (6)
21. Wipes out. (6)
22. Cathedral city. (3)
23. Litigate. (3)
24. Plaything. (3)

Down
1. Without making an error. (2, 7)
2. Image. (4)
3. Get up speed. (6, 3)
4. Refuse. (4, 4)
5. Grub. (5)
6. Scare. (4)
7. Without finish. (9)
8. French coin. (3)
10. American middle west. (4, 4)
14. To do with the p o wer of the m o on. (5)

15. Spanish labourers. (5)
16. Slashes. (4)
18. Colour. (4)

Across
1. Fight line (anag.). (5, 4)
9. Top card. (3)
11. M-way. (5-4)
12. Barbarian. (3)
13. Irish jig for instance. (4-5)

Small Crosswords 20.

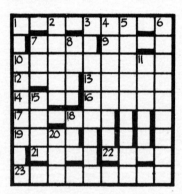

17. Group of huts for travellers. (6)
19. German boy's name. (4)
21. From the grocery. (4)
22. Caledonian. (4)
23. Moss trial (anag). (9)

Down
1. For the visitor. (5, 4)
2. It bisects your arm. (5)
3. It is sometimes a problem for a growing youngster. (3, 6)
4. Dangerous. (8)
5. Modern schools all study this subject. (9)
6. A few bits of advice. (4, 5)
7. Old measure. (3)
8. Genuflects. (4)
11. Size of a book. (6)
15. Used by porridge-makers. (4)

18. Toothed wheel. (3)
20. Pitch. (3)

Across
1. Tasty, with duck. (5, 4)
7. German river. (4)
9. Sound return. (4)
10. Ample space. (5, 4)
12. Tardy. (4)
13. After that time. (5)
14. Pulls. (4)
16. Material. (5)

Small Crosswords

Small Crosswords 21.

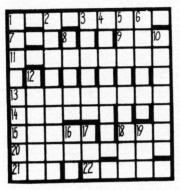

11. Icy patch. (4, 5)
13. Amalgamated. (9)
14. Strong. (6)
15. Scent. (5) 18. Sheep. (3)
20. Dismal events. (9)
21. Attempt. (3)
22. Tidies a room. (5)

Down
1. Weather man. (4, 5)
2. Good Rugby player? (5, 4)
3. Model girls. (6)
4. Pearl set (anag.). (8)
5. Sluggi h quality. (9)
6. Cried. (6)
8. Good-bye. (5)
10. Pro mises. (7)
12. Hi ma layan cedar. (6)
16. Girl's name. (3)
17. Communist. (3)
19. Damp. (3)

Across
1. Reasonable, all things considered including the cost in the first place. (4, 5)
7. Fuss. (3)
9. Card game. (3)

Small Crosswords 22.

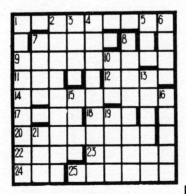

17. Carry. (4)
18. Chess piece. (3)
20. Brings into use. (8)
22. Debatable. (4)
23. Thread. (5)
24. Writer. (3)
25. Annoys in a petty way. (6)

Down
1. Remains of a forest giant. (4-5)
2. Order. (9)
3. Exclusively. (4)
4. Feature of Edinburgh. (5, 4)
5. French coin. (3)
6. Makes a mistake. (4)
7. Full-skirted dress. (4)
8. Monster lake. (4, 4)
10. Farm crop. (3)
13. Sc rap. (6)
15. Spent salmon. (4)
16. Part of a building. (5)
19. Conti nent. (4)
21. Part of the foot. (3)

Across
1. Rode tours (anag). (5, 4)
7. One kind of key. (5)
9. Say five a.m. (5, 4)
11. Devon river. (3)
12. Parliament provides them. (4)
14. Green, possibly. (6, 3)

23

Small Crosswords

Small Crosswords 23.

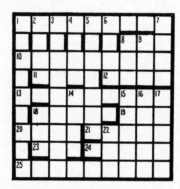

Across
1. Get the advantage. (5, 4)
8. Part of India. (3)
10. Hateful. (9)
11. Standard. (4)
12. Colours. (4)
13. Deceivers. (3-6)
18. Facade. (5)
19. Contend. (3)
20. Encounter. (4)
21. Farmyard fowl. (5)
23. Before. (3)
24. Cooked in an oven. (5)
25. Set errors (Anag.) (9)

Down
1. Casual employee. (4-5)
2. Rock hazard. (4)
3. They seek out little-known places. (9)
4. Sea-bird. (4)
5. Drooping. (7)   6. Fist. (4)
7. Dines. (4)   8. Happy. (3)
9. Single. (3)   14. Carry. (4)
15. Call forth. (5)
16. Staircase tread. (5)
17. Embryos. (5)
18. Payment. (3)
22. Paddle. (3)

Small Crosswords 24.

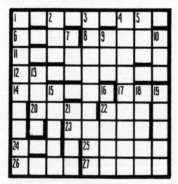

Across
1. Memory of the blitz. (4, 5)
6. Weaving machine. (4)
8. Monastery chief. (5)
11. For the aid of injured. (9)
12. Made a remark. (9)
14. Dressing gown-like garment. (6)
17. Heavy cup. (3)
20. Fill the breech. (4)
22. Material. (3)
23. Sums given for a time. (5)
24. Possess. (3)
25. Say. (5)
26. Loving caress. (4)
27. Remains. (5)

Down
1. One that contains all the names of offending footballers? (5, 4)
2. Crowd. (3)
3. Magnificence. (9)
4. Unguents. (9)
5. Fabulous bird. (3)
7. Silent. (3)
9. Hurried. (3)
10. Colour. (3)
13. Greasy. (4)
15. Sounds of pain. (5)
16. Speechify. (5)
18. Irritated. (5)
19. Mechanical matters. (5)
21. Beers. (4)

24

Small Crosswords

Look out for further puzzle books by Tim McKay.

Small Crosswords 25.

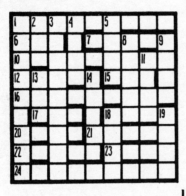

12. Gowns. (5)
15. Girl's name. (3)
16. Selection by us. (3, 6)
17. Hint. (3)   18. Behalf. (4)
20. Knot. (4)
21. Boundary. (5)
22. Number. (5)   23. Peer. (4)
24. Kent port. (9)

Down

1. Quite a stand-up fight. (3, 6)
2. Wonder. (3)
3. London station. (3, 6)
4. Leisure. (4)
5. Time for bargains. (4)
8. Madness. (5)
9. Foot-wear. (4)
11. Bag. (4)
13. No longer b atting. (3)
14. M o v e. (5)
18. G l imp-sed. (4)
19. Fish. (4)

Across

1. Make yourself comfortable. (4, 1, 4)
6. Sheep. (3)
7. Slopes. (5)
10. Latest report. (4-5)

Small Crosswords 26.

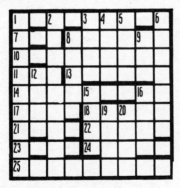

14. By plane or helicopter. (3, 6)
17. Flower. (4)
18. Bird of prey. (5)
21. Close. (4)
22. Proof : not guilty. (5)
23. Containers. (4)
24. Pistol-maker. (5)
25. Times sips (anag.). (9)

Down

1. Start of the show. 7, 2)
2. German provincials. (9)
3. Number. (4)
4. Sunken fence. (2-2)
5. Vivacity. (4)
6. She lured men to destruction by her song. (7)
8. Takes his ease. (5)
9. T witch. (3)
12. T h e .Emerald Isle. (4)
15. Genuine. (4)
16. G erman r i v er. (4)
19. M ineral s alt s. (4)
20. F amous f i l m. (4)

Across

1. From the Caribbean . . . shapely—but may let you down ! (5, 4)
7. Girl's name. (3)
8. Marble bridge of Venice. (6)
10. Black locks. (5, 4)
11. Refreshing drink. (3)
13. Spiritualist service. (6)

Small Crosswords

Keep up the crossword habit each day with the Daily Express.

Small Crosswords 27.

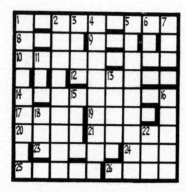

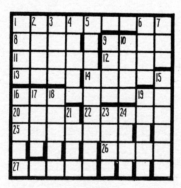

17. Fish. (4)
19. American coin. (4)
20. Smooth. (4)
21. Low-down cubans ? (5)
23. Shakespeare's forest. (5)
24. Decay. (3)
25. Medicinal amounts. (5)
26. Glimpse. (4)

Down

1. Cromwellian. (9)
2. Cartographers. (3-6)
3. Victim of animal hunting for food. (4)
4. Expands. (9)
5. Testers of knowledge. (9)
6. Girl's name. (3)
7. Small goat. (3)
11. Baked item. (3)
13. Polish. (5)
15. Split. (4)
16. Windy. (5)
18. Miss Gardner. (3)
22. Cut. (3)

Across

1. Tasty cut of meat. (4, 5)
8. Old poet. (4)
9. Impost. (3)
10. Winning way. (5, 4)
12. Weakly acquiescent person. (3-3)
14. Loveable person. (4, 5)

Small Crosswords 28.

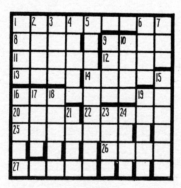

20. Difficult. (4)
22. Flower. (5)
25. Lacking plumpness. (7)
26. Sense. (4)
27. Pool of winnings. (5)

Down

1. Digging creature. (4)
2. Amongst. (4)
3. Telephoned (4)
4. Irish colour. (5)
5. Target relative. (4, 5)
6. Girl's name. (4)
7. Optic. (3)
9. Liner. (4)
10. Mounted game. (4)
15. Amble. (6)
16. Show gratitude. (5)
17. Status. (5)
18. Slang. (5)
19. Allude (5)
21. Powder. (4)
23. Strong box. (4)
24. Found in the wood. (4)

Across

1. Marine rag (anag). (9)
8. Old poet. (4)
9. Salmon river. (4)
11. Pillow cases and so on. (5)
12. Orifice. (4)
13. Rum. (4)
14. Ploughs. (5)
16. Troopship. (5)

Small Crosswords

Small Crosswords 29.

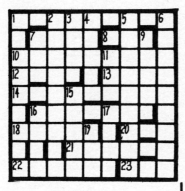

14. Smoke. (9)
16. Water ousels. (7)
18. Bucolic. (5)
20. Age. (3)　**21.** Sanity. (6)
22. Order. (6)
23. Dismal. (3)

Down
1. For rubbish. (4-5)
2. Stores assistants. (4-5)
3. Feature of the skin. (4)
4. Wild British animal. (5)
5. Siren. (9)
6. Rhythm orchestra. (5, 4)
7. Secret agent. (3)
9. Carol singers. (5)
11. Bishopric. (3)
15. Separately. (5)
16. Customs or excise payment. (4)
17. Cheese from Holland. (4)
19. Shelter. (3)

Across
1. Drop tides (anag.). (9)
7. Fired. (4)
8. Morning moisture. (3)
10. Athlete. (9)
12. Printers' metal. (4)
13. Long poem. (4)

Small Crosswords 30.

20. Less muscular. (6)
21. Resort. (3)
22. Something of worth. (5)
23. Bunches of feathers—or hair. (5)
24. Taste. (3)

Down
1. Building term for wall-coating of lime and gravel. (5, 4)
2. Canadian emblem. (5, 4)
3. Imitated. (4)
4. Tear. (3)
5. Clothes warmer. (5)
6. Song. (5)
7. Nozzle. (5)
8. Royalty. (8)
9. Served on Shrove Tuesday. (8)
14. Kill that fly. (4)
16. Part of the brewery. (4)
17. Solidify. (3)
18. Journey. (4)

Across
1. Old thoroughfare. (5, 4)
7. Vital fluid. (3)
8. Seed. (3)
10. Top half (5, 4)
11. Valuable metal. (4)
12. Tavern. (3)
13. Hunt. (3, 3, 3)
15. Shore. (5)
19. Era. (3)

Small Crosswords

Small Crosswords 31.

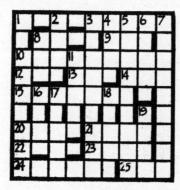

15. Devises. (7)
20. Large birds. (4)
21. Musical instrument. (4)
22. Prison room. (4)
23. Stitched. (4)
24. Names. (6) 25. Sister. (3)

Down

1. Building expert. (9)
2. Staff. (4)
3. Distinctive facial feature. (5, 4)
4. So let it be. (4)
5. Destroys. (5, 4)
6. Complete. (5)
7. Dark thought. (9)
8. Bird noise. (3)
11. Girl's apparel. (5)
16. Reputation, especially if good. (4)
17. Cellar. (5)
18. Underground trains. (5)
19. Bill of fare. (4)

Across

1. Mechanical gear. (9)
8. Famous clown. (4)
9. Encountered. (3)
10. Often served for supper. (4, 5)
12. Garden item. (3)
13. Hurried. (3)
14. Material. (3)

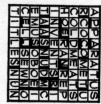

Small Crosswords 32.

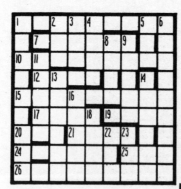

21. Catalogue of names. (4)
24. Cheddar or Cheshire product. (6)
25. Beer. (3)
26. Ceremonial act. (4, 5)

Down

1. Hard lines. (5, 4)
2. Everyone. (3)
3. Declare. (3)
4. On credit. (4)
5. Farm animal. (3)
6. Kiev's Gold (anag.). (9)
8. Part of the forest. (4)
9. Work it out. (5)
11. Weekend bags. (5)
13. Says yes. (6)
14. He makes the formal announcements. (6)
16. Orifices. (5)
18. Deep plate. (4)
22. Ocean. (3)
23. Sunbrown. (3)

Across

1. On the breakfast table. (5-4)
7. Weaves. (6)
10. Menacing mob. (4, 5)
12. Standing. (4)
15. Top flight. (4, 5)
17. Push with a stick. (4)
19. Brave man. (4)
20. Employ. (3)

Small Crosswords

The Small Crosswords will help your children with their spelling.

Small Crosswords 33.

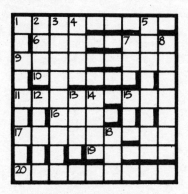

11. Little girl enjoys playing with this. (5, 4)
16. Security for court appearance. (4)
17. Given information. (9)
19. Periods of time. (5)
20. A vision of great beauty. (5, 4)

Down

1. The finish of civilisation. (6, 3)
2. Scottish town. (4)
3. Colour. (5, 4)
4. Tie. (4)
5. Firearm capable of shooting additional bullets. (8)
7. Fish eggs. (3)
8. Parson's dissertations. (7)
12. Possessor. (5)
13. Deposited. (4)
14. Deep breath. (4)
15. Decay. (3)
18. Pig. (3)

Across

1. Like the Mona Lisa—or any girl's face. (4, 2, 3)
6. They are fed daily by many gardeners. (8)
9. It is always there it is said, where there is life. (3, 2, 4)
10. Good one in a friend is a thing to be cherished. (6)

Small Crosswords 34.

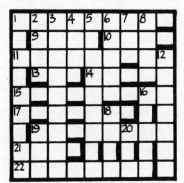

17. Musical composition. (7)
19. Automobile contests. (3, 5)
21. Annoy. (4)
22. Very small. (4-4)

Down

1. Armoured aid to infantry. (5, 4)
2. Listeners. (4)
3. Special attention. (5, 4)
4. Elderly. (4)
5. Distance to walk. (4, 5)
6. Made additions to the fluid reserves. (3, 2)
7. Night before. (3)
8. Genuine. (4)
12. Relative by marriage. (7)
16. Bloodsucker. (5)
18. Carriage for hire. (4)
19. Tin. (3)
20. Projection on gear wheel. (3)

Across

7. Law expression. (5, 4)
9. Ship in which Jason sailed. (4)
10. Part of a cooker. (4)
11. On the menu. (5, 4)
13. Dismal. (3)
14 Culpability. (5)
15. Indian sign. (5, 4)

Small Crosswords

Small Crosswords 35.

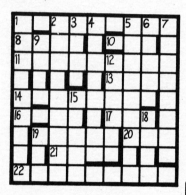

side of the ship. (3, 5)
16. Birthplace of Goliath. (4)
17. Carp. (3)
19. Broom. (5)
20. Take a nap. (3)
21. Regrets. (4)
22. Grows longer (9)

Down

1. Neighbourhood child. (5, 4)
2. No profit. (3, 6)
3. Frigid. (4)
4. Summer fog. (4, 4)
5. Self-confidence. (9)
6. Not here. (5)
7. New York district. (4, 4)
9. Expectation and desire. (4)
12. Rings up. (6)
15. Shoulder movement. (5)
18. Formal dress. (4)
19. Payment. (3)

Across

1. Midday engagement. (5, 4)
8. American State. (4)
10. Tree. (3)
11. Gives away (9)
13. Injured. (4)
14. Land not on the weather

Small Crosswords 36.

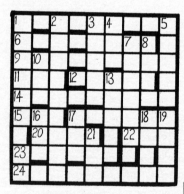

15. Consume. (3)
17. Express doubts about opponents' bridge bid. (6)
20. Musical instrument. (4)
22. Cover. (3)
23. Mountain systems. (6)
24. Hazardous situation. (5, 4)

Down

1. Be brave. (4, 5)
2. Separating infected patient from others. (9)
3. Traditional early morning naval call. (5)
4. Help. (3)
5. Longed. (5)
7. Prominent. (7)
8. Graceful bird. (4)
10. Indication of a girl's maiden name. (3)
13. Closes. (5)
16. Miss Gardner. (3)
17. Hound. (3)
18. Bathing place. (4)
19. Prepare for publication. (4)
21. Allow. (3)

Across

1. Advice to luggage handler that is not always noticed. (4, 3, 2)
6. Refrains from drinking. (8)
9. Auction term. (5, 4)
11. Fish. (3)
12. Roman goddess of the hearth. (5)
14. Clumsy person has one. (5, 4)

Small Crosswords

Small Crosswords 37.

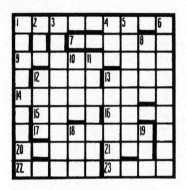

Across

1. Write a note. (4, 1, 4)
7. Royal headband. (6)
9. Flummoxed. (2, 3, 4)
12. Trick. (4)
13. Scottish tribe. (4)
14. Take exercise. (4, 1, 4)
15. Stalk. (4)

16. Volcano. (4)
17. Late meals. (7)
20. Boy's name. (5)
21. Grain crop. (3)
22. Colour. (5)
23. Ship's timber. (4)

Down

1. Doubt Alec (anag.). (6-3)
2. Tear. (3)
3. In the wrong place. (3, 2, 4)
4. Part of a race. (3)
5. Worship of graven images. (8)
6. Demon rate (anag.). (9)
8. Impetuosity. (4)
10. In tense dislike. (4)
11. Pattern. (7)
12. Sibilance. (4)
13. Hurrahs. (6)
18. Swine. (3)
19. Ocean. (3)

Small Crosswords 38.

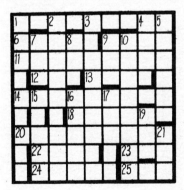

Across

1. Soaring ambitions. (4, 5)
6. State of America. (5)
9. Crippled. (4)
11. Marked by the gong, perhaps. (4, 5)
12. Writer. (3)
13. Amount owed. (4)
14. Peremptory. (9)

18. News agency man. (6)
20. Intense love. (9)
22. Well-behaved. (4)
23. Single. (3)
24. Welsh boy's name. (5)
25. At the present. (3)

Down

1. Selection of top tunes. (3, 6)
2. Apartment for pastimes. (5-4)
3. Retain for immediate use. (4, 5)
4. Give out. (4)
5. Breed of dog. (6)
7. Bathe. (3)
8. Fowl. (3)
9. Untruth. (3)
10. Desire to seek after fame. (8)
15. Marsh plant. (5)
16. Mistake. (5)
17. Ballet dancers' skirts. (5)
19. Age. (3)
21. Novel. (3)

31

Small Crosswords

While-away your moments with Tim McKay's puzzles.

Small Crosswords 39.

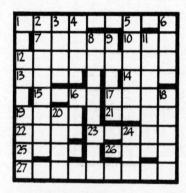

Across
1. Hot tea mug (anag.). (5, 4)
7. Therefore. (5)
8. Imitate. (3)
9. Motorway repairs. (4, 5)
10. Lamentable encounter. (3, 3)
14. Subsequently. (5)
15. Pal. (4)
16. Roman emperor. (4)
18. Mail. (4)   19. Optic. (3)
20. Nightmares. (6)

Down
1. Exciting. (9)
2. Not changed. (9)
3. Wood-cutter. (5)
4. Debatable. (4)
5. Creature found in the soil. (5-4)
6. Cricket international. (4, 5)
11. Cavalry soldier. (6)
12. Happy. (5)
13. Money bags. (6)
15. Dried coconut. (5)
17. Untreated metal. (3)

Small Crosswords 40.

Across
1. Midday meals. (9)
7. Unpleasant expressions. (5)
10. Rodent. (3)
12. Waste Nero (anag.). (9)
13. Colour. (4)   14. Lid. (3)
15. Scrooge-like. (4)
17. Dismal. (4)
19. Sweeps. (4)
21. Irish. (4)
22. American State. (4)
23. Loosens. (5)
25. Give for a time. (4)
26. Most perfect. (4)
27. Last days. (9)

Down
1. Departed spirits. (4, 5)
2. Final. (8)
3. Kind of gas. (4)
4. American coin. (4)
5. Speaker. (6)
6. Pace. (4)
8. Antlered animals. (8)
9. Vegetable. (5)
11. Awakens. (7)
16. Kind of tree. (3)
18. Reposes. (5)
20. Bombastic talk. (4)
24. Ocean. (3)

Small Crosswords

Small Crosswords 41.

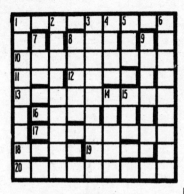

13. Small part. (6, 3)
16. Hurry. (4)
17. More muscular. (8)
18. Always. (4)
19. Belonging to us. (4)
20. Assistants. (4-5)

Down

1. Those of a cat, perhaps. (4, 5)
2. Meditated. (9)
3. For hanging meat carcasses. (5, 4)
4. Narrow lanes with stables. (4)
5. Individuality. (3)
6. Go alternately. (4, 5)
7. Lubricate. (3)
8. Reports. (5)
9. Glorifies. (7)
14. Tiredness. (5)
15. Luggage. (3)

Across

1. Opinions not required. (2, 7)
8. Descry. (3)
10. Labour after dark. (5, 4)
11. Old Testament figure. (3)
12. Part of a brewery. (4)

Small Crosswords 42.

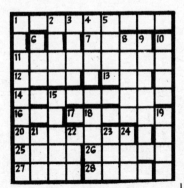

20. Existing at the beginning. (7)
25. French city. (4)
26. Honourable fame. (5)
27. Happiness. (4)
28. Paving stone. (4)

Down

1. Ban on parking. (2, 7)
2. Attention. (4)
3. Landlord of inn. (4)
4. News detail in journal. (4)
5. Select flowers—or animals from herd. (4)
6. Plunder. (3)
8. Person entertained. (5)
9. Distribute. (7)
10. For winter sports enthusiasts. (4)
15. Moment. (5)
18. Fits up. (4)
19. Spinning toy. (4)
21. Nothing. (3)
22. Golf item. (3)
23. Beer. (3)
24. A person's destiny. (3)

Across

1. More elderly than it would seem. (2, 7)
7. Pulls. (4)
11. By misfortune. (5, 4)
12. Assist. (4)
13. Meadow. (3)
14. Private concerns. (9)
16. Sailor. (3)
17. Good-looking. (6)

33

Small Crosswords

Small Crosswords 43.

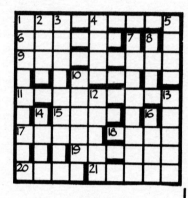

Across

1. For your comfort in cinemas and theatres. (3-2, 4)
6. Using the line. (2, 4)
9. Country's flag. 5, 4)
10. Remain. (4)

11. Hunt. (3, 3, 3,)
15. Zoo animal. (4)
17. Distemper. (5)
18. Singing artist. (4)
19. Fear. (6)
20. Mites. (4)
21. Places. (5)

Down

1. Difficult situation. (5 4)
2. Taverns. (4)
3. Catalogue. (5, 4)
4. Measure. (4)
5. Profit. (4)
7. Woo. (3, 5)
8. Blemish. (4)
10. Southampton footballers. (6)
12. Short letters. (5)
13. Sincerely to end a letter. (5)
14. Aura. (4)
16. Bitter fruit. (4)

Small Crosswords 44.

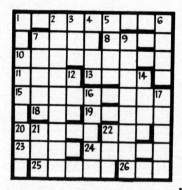

Across

1. Snack, perhaps. (5, 4)
7. Timber. (4)
8. Force of African fighters. (4)
10. Become rancid. (4, 5)
11. Animal cry. (4)
13. Despatched. (4)
15 In the bathroom. (5, 4)
18. Dog or cat. (3)

19. Corner. (5)
20. Biscuits, perhaps. (5)
22. Driving spot. (3)
23. Unusual. (4)
24. Coarse cloth. (5)
25. Modern material. (5)
26. Title. (3)

Down

1. Simple labours. (5, 4)
2. Become tired. (4, 5)
3. Cut timber. (3)
4. Hardy heroine. (4)
5. Baby. (4)
6. Untruths. (4)
7. Body of soldiers. (5)
9. Bosses. (8)
12. Allow. (3)
14. Ceramic plate. (4)
16. Lariat. (5)
17. Sufferer from a tropical disease. (5)
21. Commercial. vehicle. (3)
22. Half a score. (3)

Small Crosswords

Small Crosswords 45.

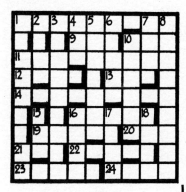

16. Stagger. (5)   19. Wait. (5)
20. Word of agreement. (3)
21. Rodent. (3)
22. Long-handled spoon. (5)
23. Give up. (5)
24. Water-and-soap mixture. (4)

Down
1. Romantic tale. (4, 5)
2. Leave out. (4)
3. Work till all hours. (3, 2, 4)
4. Refreshing drink. (3)
5. Unfeeling. (7)
6. Wall-tapestry. (5)
7. Do a deal. (4)
8. Introduces power. (9)
10. Insurance paper. (6)
15. Health resort. (3)
16. Quiet moment. (4)
17. Communists. (4)
18. Attention. (4)

Across
1. Defeated law suit. (4, 5)
9. Listener. (3)
10. Writer. (3)
11. Important part. (5, 4)
12. Needle-case. (4)
13. Everyone. (3)
14. Imagining. (9)

Small Crosswords 46.

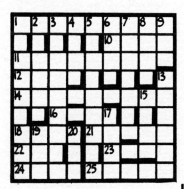

18. Trees. (4)
21. How to enjoy a good breakfast. (3, 2)
22. Descry. (3)
23. Powder. (4)
24. Carol. (4)
25. Horse laugh. (5)

Down
1. Clever estimate. (4, 5)
2. Sound of explosion. (6)
3. Football team. (6, 3)
4. Girl's name. (4)
5. Invisible. (3, 6)
6. Part of church. (4)
7. Graceful. (7)
8. Direct one's way. (4)
9. Act like a jelly on the tennis court. (3)
13. Drawing. (6)
15. Line. (4)
17. Strong dislike. (4)
19. The lion. (3)
20. Droop. (3)

Across
1. The intelligence is superb. (5, 4)
10. In the shelter. (4)
11. Entries in this are unrestricted. (4, 5)
12. Bird of peace. (4)
14. Londoners love it. (5, 4)
16. Great architect. (4)

Small Crosswords

Small Crosswords 47.

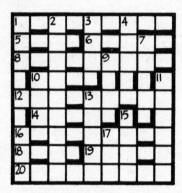

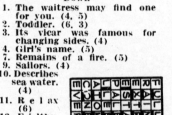

Across
1. Complete flowering. (4, 5)
5. Shower. (4)
6. Regulations. (5)
8. A d d i t i o nal opportunities. (5, 4)
10. Remain. (4)

12. Light colour. (4, 5)
14. Unpleasant expressions. (5)
16. The present era. (6, 3)
18. Fir tree seed. (4)
19. Stupid person. (5)
20. Good radio enables ~ou to hear ! (5, 4)

Down
1. The waitress may find one for you. (4, 5)
2. Toddler. (6, 3)
3. Its vicar was famous for changing sides. (4)
4. Girl's name. (5)
7. Remains of a fire. (5)
9. Sailors. (4)
10. Describes sea water. (4)
11. R e l ax (6)
13. F i lthy. (5)
15. G a m- b l i ng game. (4)
17. F a r m a n imal. (3)

Small Crosswords 48.

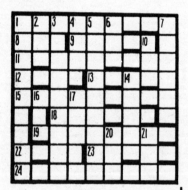

Across
1. Important operator. (3, 6)
8. Night before. (3)
9. Stay. (5)
11. Dining or lunching. (6, 3)
12. Important golf stroke. (4)
13. Dance. (5)
15. Halt in good time. (4, 5)
18. Band of warriors. (6)

19. Mount for exciting game. (4, 4)
22. Crippled. (4)
23. Unreasoning fear. (5)
24. Remains unmoving. (4, 5)

Down
1. Stay unmoving. (4, 5)
2. Girl's name. (3)
3. Still to happen. (3, 2, 4)
4. Serve at table. (4)
5. Possesses retail establishments. (4, 5)
6. Torn cloth. (3)
7. Turn. (6)
10. Bath. (3)
14. Adult whose mental development has been arrested. (5)
16. D u mp for refuse. (3)
17. R o d s a n d p erches. (5)
20. S m a ll q u a n- tity of b u tter. (3)
21. N o t h- ing at all. (3)

Sunshine Puzzles

We supply you with the words, all you have to do is find the right place for them in the grid.

Here are the words to go in the grid

Annulment   Arbutus
Fulminate   Among
Interment   Ennui
Paregoric   End up
Privateer   Lupin
Monstrous   Stiff
Empirical   Plies
Damson pie   Lucre
Waterfall   Tinny
Tentative   Biped
Impulsion
Telephony
Aniseed
Alerted
Hustler
Nuclear
Deepens
Toddler
Towpath

Sunshine Puzzles 1.

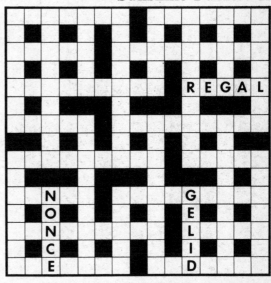

The words for No. 2 puzzle

King of the castle   Resin
Atrocious   Sneak
Attracted   Split
Catechist   State
Empirical   Stork
Rate Books   Wrung
Enrapture   Form
Fortunate
Hermitage
Interpret
Mean theft
Ornaments
Startling
Ashen
Aster
Crime
Grape
Islam
Irate

Sunshine Puzzles 2.

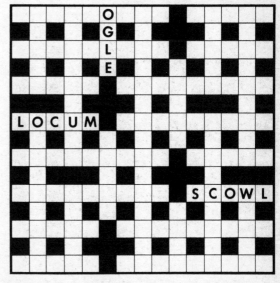

Sunshine Puzzles

All these go into grid No. 3

Decadence	Tactics
Different	Tresses
Equipment	Puddles
Farmstead	Crisp
Inclusive	Dared
Oversight	Larks
Political	Nerve
Regularly	Paste
Supersede	Plume
Truncated	Tally
Catspaw	
Deplore	
Dresser	
Dusters	
Elderly	
Encored	
Entails	
Impulse	
Salient	

Sunshine Puzzles 3.

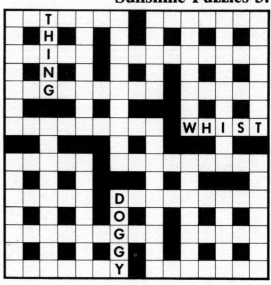

Notice the clue words to help you

At the drop of a hat	Bell
Auto-biographies	Inks
Top of the morning	Hats
Sword-swallowing	Hips
Condiment	Also
Landscape	Mica
Propagate	Opal
Represent	Oval
Avenger	Ours
Corkage	Stew
Cherish	Ace
Gherkin	Eli
Hairnet	
Deanery	
Implore	
Oilpipe	
Riposte	
Soprano	
Area	

Sunshine Puzzles 4.

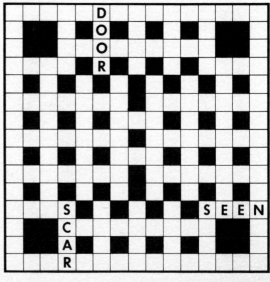

Sunshine Puzzles

Crosswords help to widen your vocabulary.

You have to work a miracle in this one.

Sunshine Puzzles 5.

Coalition
Magnitude
Motorists
Nightmare
Objection
Universal
Adjunct
Assault
Dragoon
Egotism
Expanse
Earthen
Elevate
Miracle
Tunnels
Utilise
Valance
Village
Curio
Digit
Ennui
Fiend
Lover
Lurch
Nippy
Salad
Tryst
Able
Here
Nark
Pisa
Rate
Sack
Scar

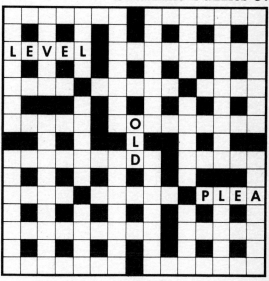

Vodka is one clue here.

Sunshine Puzzles 6.

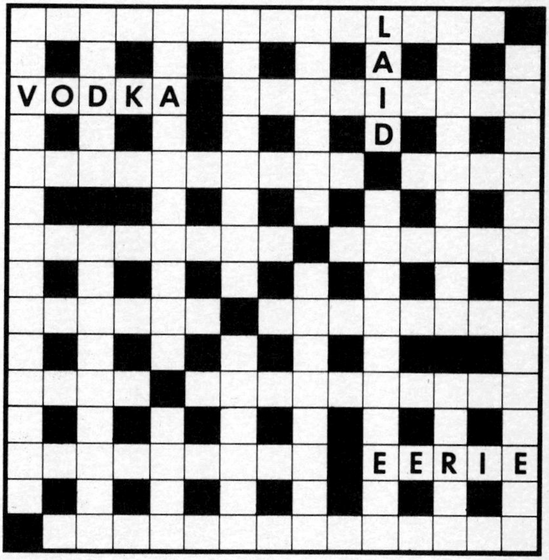

Breathlessness
Lord chancellor
Love-in-Idleness
Precociousness
Chorister
Condiments
Fathomless
Clamminess
Ironmoulds
Situation
Ostracise
Mutilator
Imminent
Cashmere
Cloudy
Famish
Latest
Accruing
Fandango
Zodiac
Nerve
Talc
Rodeo
Null
Gala

Sunshine Puzzles

You're in good company with Tim McKay.

Don't get upset in the wrong place here!

Ambulance
Carpenter
Emigrated
Graduates
Abandons
Greyness
Redeemed
Released
Seashore
Stutters
Scotched
Thunders
Accept
Abound
Asters
Exotic
Engage
Editor
Gusted
Desire
Spouts
Stroke
Waster
Garden
Adept
Ember
Ernie
Ledge
Nicer
Nurse
Sweet
Upset
Pea

Sunshine Puzzles 7.

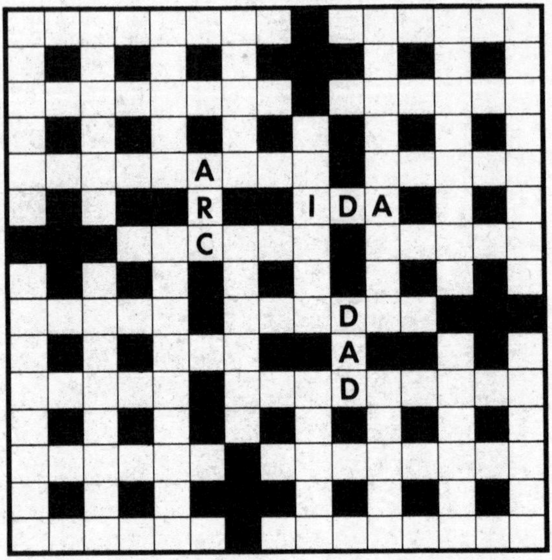

Here are the clues for No. 8

Disconsolately
Investigations
Queen of Sheba
Constitution
Descendant
Silver coin
Conductor
Remainder
Galvanise
Oil tanker
Operettas
Rumblings
Cultures
Samovars
Address
Atomise
Asides
Lyrics
Stream
Robust
Ovate
Bilge
Arcs
Lard
Scan

Sunshine Puzzles 8.

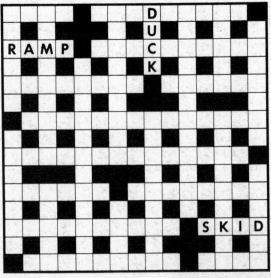

Sunshine Puzzles

Almost 10,000 puzzles and Tim McKay still goes strong.

You must get Inexact exactly right for this one

Statistical
Self-centred
Achromatic
Three-score
Cauterise
Secretary
Sovereign
Red-headed
Cathedral
Betrothed
Emigrate
Enchased
Ascetic
Inexact
Fog-horn
Lapdogs
Younger

Refined
Giggles
Cashier
Drill
Avenge
Course
Audit
Abhor
Mitre
Abel
Call
Sum

Sunshine Puzzles 9.

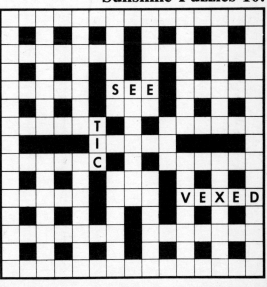

Top marks if you've managed all the others!

Jack of all trades
Jam for breakfast
Superintendents
The Daily Express
Canners
Dilutes
Envelop
Oilcake
Inertia
On-drive
Earache
Roomier
Textile
Aviator
Bullion
Mangler
Trollop
Arrest
Basket

Enable
Exotic
Gentle
Latter
Spiral
Prison
Image
Inter
Kedge
Opera
Pen
She
Tar
Peg

Sunshine Puzzles 10.

Monkey Puzzles

These are more difficult than the Sunshine Puzzles for they have no printed-in clues at all. Fill in the Squares from this list. For solutions turn to the list at the back of the book.

Monkey Puzzles 1.

Apparatus	Asters
Commander	Elders
Extortion	Employ
Irritated	Heaths
Blasted	Shards
Drovers	Strewn
Eatable	Tested
Embargo	Welder
Embroil	Inner
Emperor	Olive
Encores	Pence
Overdue	Rated
Parleys	Strum
Pastime	Tempo
Relents	Art
Rooster	Hew
Russets	Sin
Sophist	Spy
Timbers	
Whistle	

Monkey Puzzles 2.

Entertainment	Enrol
Railway tracks	Ideas
Assimilate	Inter
Sunday best	Opera
Inventive	Apes
Scenarios	Axis
Adenoids	Isle
Pleasure	Nail
Resident	Obey
Stresses	Scan
Stricken	Scar
Tolerate	Wits
Dresser	Tat
Respect	
Basset	
Envies	
Prison	
Sitter	
Strips	
Trysts	

Monkey Puzzles

Monkey Puzzles 3.

Original price	Trapeze
Preternatural	Unaware
Automatic	Action
Gentleman	Throng
Net Weight	Eager
No contest	Elder
Applied	Regal
Compass	Rusty
Elastic	Water
Gelatin	Wiser
Imagery	Ems
Meaning	Era
Nodular	Eve
Realism	Lot
Red hair	Too
Remnant	Wee
Rocking	
Stencil	
The pair	
Trample	

Monkey Puzzles 4.

Entertainments	Alert
Indecipherable	Fluff
Recommendation	Lord
Terror-stricken	Miss
Emphatic	Rack
Impudent	Sour
Inscribe	
Pleasure	
Snuffled	
Sternums	
Acuity	
Admits	
Entire	
Gallop	
Lashed	
Lotion	
Nested	
Pellet	
Speech	
Trifle	

Monkey Puzzles

Monkey Puzzles 5.

Adding machine	Hyena
Scientologist	Plump
People in tents	React
The Last Supper	Recap
Accounted	Aida
Exonerate	Brie
Last scene	Eats
Salacious	Espy
Adhering	Pink
Lonesome	Sloe
Lancelot	
Succeeds	
Elapsed	
On earth	
Poison	
Stands	
Sonata	
Topper	
Again	
Chess	

Monkey Puzzles 6.

Advertisement	Scatter
Street traders	Seafire
Court hearing	Servant
Short measure	Tornado
Addressee	Asses
Harvester	Refer
Shattered	Scant
Transient	Teeny
Attires	Cad
Despair	Cos
Erudite	Eft
Expound	Ire
Flutter	Nut
Granite	Oft
Inroads	Pad
Matures	Vie
Nirvana	
Obscure	
Readily	
Repeals	

44

Monkey Puzzles

Monkey Puzzles 7.

Parallelograms
Progressionist
Speechlessness
Transcendental
Abortive
Amending
Anathema
Dogmatic
Emulsion
Optician
Ruggedly
Trailers
Albion
Argued
Cinema
Dreams
Endear
Fondle
Greedy
Grooms

Ideals
Indeed
Jocose
Scolds
Grid
Evil
Lily
Song

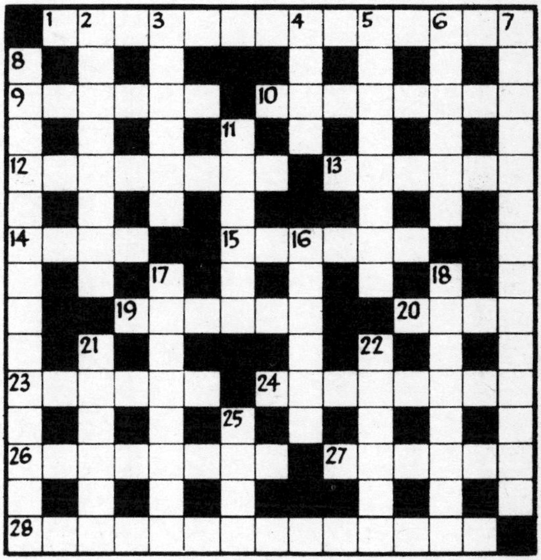

Monkey Puzzles 8.

Battle-scarred
Commemoration
Air freight
Competitor
Afterward
Fanatical
Prolific
Underlay
Asphalt
Attired
Clamour
Imprint
Marital
Neither
Proverb
Recount
Remoter
Actors
Mature
Parrot

Sprain
Extra
Rumba
Beta
Cost
Mite
Pain
Coy
Fat
Oaf
Oil
Our
Yes

Monkey Puzzles

Don't let the Monkey Puzzles make a monkey out of you.

Monkey Puzzles 9.

Christenings
Unadvertised
Expressions
Theatre seat
Intercept
Necklaces
Police dog
Pretences
Situation
Stipulate
Surrender
Telephone
Barterer
Disaster
Expended
Famished
Atoned
Flinty
Gasped
Resist

Alike
Isles
Motes
Pests
Ricks
Spied
Taste
Upset
Dip
Ire

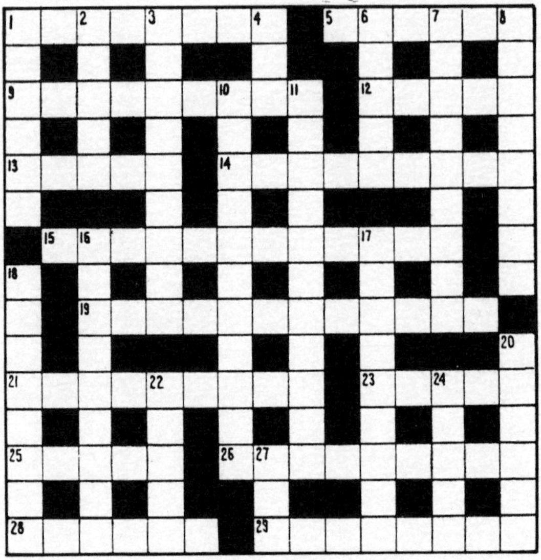

Monkey Puzzles 10.

Asseveration
Consequences
Good question
Tesselations
Chilterns
Courtesan
Dispenses
Envisages
Outlasted
Overacted
Ownership
Scarlatti
Dissuade
Preserve
Slap down
Speedhog
Blocks
Eldest
Swerve
Temple

Altar
Anvil
Ether
Larva
Lyres
Rouse
These
Value

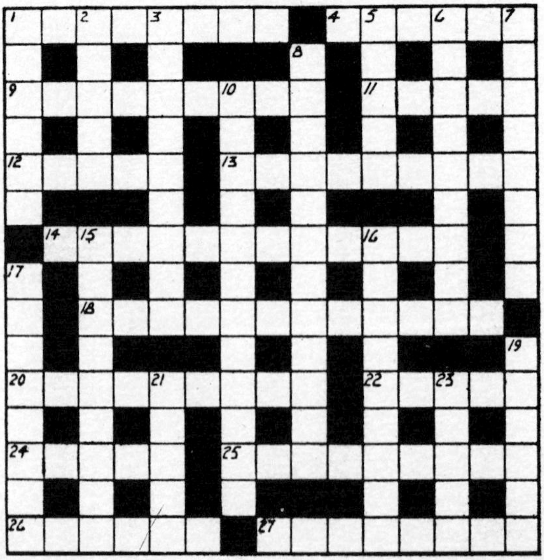

The Make You Very *Cross*-Words

THESE have only one clue numbered — the first — both Across and Down. None of the others are in their correct order. SOME HINTS: First read all the clues and concentrate on those with an unusual letter-count. For instance if there is only one eight letter word you can easily find its position in the puzzle. When you have chosen a word to fit, crosscheck it with the words that lead into it. In this way you can soon build up the whole puzzle . . .

The Make You Very *Cross*-Words 1.

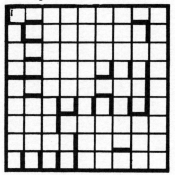

Damp. (3)
Hung. (9)
Good behaviour or manners. (8)
Horse. (5)
Insect. (6)
Part of a circle. (3)
Place of. (4)

Clues Down

Corrosion. (4)
Examined officially. (9)
Motorway police. (5, 4)
Shouts loudly. (5)
Child. (6)
Nurse. (4)
Tamed dice (anag.). (9)
Part of h a rness. (4)
Colour. (3)
U npleasing child. (4)
Before. (3)
D u r a b l e cloth. (5)
He wants to take o r d ers. (8)

Clues Across

Morn astir (anag.). (9)
Rapped lightly. (6)
Priest. (5)
They are snap-shooters, and have to be quick about it. (7)

The Make You Very *Cross*-Words 2.

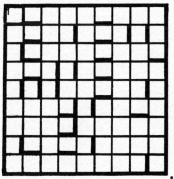

Untruth. (3)
Heads. (4)
Joint. (4)
Container. (3)
Rings. (5)
Tot of spirits. (4)
Serious defects. (5)
Acting in a dissipated fashion. (8)

Clues Down

Make love in a trifling manner. (9)
Us. (9)
Oily matter for lubricating machinery. (6)
Stream's side. (5, 4)
Beautiful girl. (4)
Out of this world. (9)
C a thedral city. (3)
There it is. o n the d i n n e r t a b l e. (4)
S l umbers. (6)
Ornamental tuft. (6)
P r i n t e r's measures. (3)

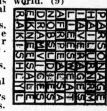

Clues Across

Many a sermon is thought up here. (9)
Cricket enthusiasts work them out. (8)
Perspiration. (5)
Expires. (4)
Disposal time at reduced prices. (4)
Weather feature. (4)

The Make You Very *Cross*-Words

You'll feel much better when you've completed the 'Make You Very Cross-words'.

The Make You Very *Cross*-Words 3.

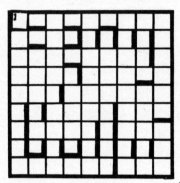

Friendly. (8)
Cut roughly. (5)
Hard fat. (4)
Charge for using bridge or ferry. (4)
Not so much. (4)
Gossip. (3)
Joke. (3)

Clues Down

Whole bean (anag.). (9)
Sounds heard behind the scenes. (6, 3)
Making big. (9)
Good works. (6)
Old ecclesiastical taxes. (6)
From oysters, perhaps or ormers. (3-6)
Case Latin scholars must be familiar with. (8)
Oven items. (4)
Italian lake. (5)
Barrel. (3)
Row. (5)

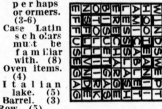

Clues Across

Exposed to the gales. (9)
Make a noise like an automobile. (4)
Before. (3)
Impetuous attack. (6)
Annoy. (3)
Pour forth. (6)

The Make You Very *Cross*-Words 4.

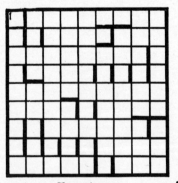

Gave its worth in pounds and pence. (9)
Beach huts. (6)
Embryo. (4)
Colour. (3)
Extremely. (4)

Clues Down

One bred for this particular fate — that has to be swallowed ! (5, 4)
Danger. (5)
Villainous. (7)
Unusual. (3)
Navigation hazard. (4)
Mountain fall. (9)
Part of armour. (5)
Campanologist. (6)
Story of a family. (4)
Un settled. (9)
One interested in radio. (8)
Descry. (3)
Swift. (6)

Clues Across

Are these entrances designed by golf course architects ? (4-5)
Containers. (4)
Misty curtain. (4)
Move home. (4)
Intense fear. (5)
Worn by a Guardsman. (8)
Cheek. (3)

48

The Make You Very *Cross*-Words

Once you're in the swing it's easy.

The Make You Very *Cross*-Words 5.

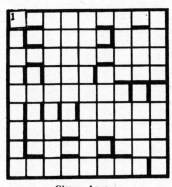

Watering place. (3)
Large shop. (5)
Knight. (3)
High naval officer. (5, 3)
Snakes. (4)
Cut. (5)
Be in debt. (3)

Clues Down

Aunt's side (anag.). (9)
Hottest day. (9)
Lectures. (9)
Vigour. (3)
Chokes off. (5)
Clever ways. (4)
Saint of Rome. (5)
Hemp for rope making. (7)
Thames at Oxford. (4)
Sketched. (5)
London district. (4)
Listening apparatus. (4)

Clues Across

Under the sea. (9)
Household machine. (4, 5)
Ridicule. (8)
May be a sharp 'un. (5)
Stags battle with them. (7)

The Make You Very *Cross*-Words 6.

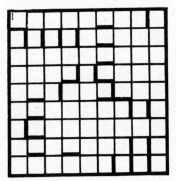

Limbs. (4)
Me, to other people. (3)
Combats. (7)
Part of the forest. (4)
Leaping with the aid of a wooden horse. (8)
Prominent. (7)

Clues Down

They are laid in the afternoon. (3-6)
On the sheltered side. (4)
Each one. (5)
Knock senseless. (4)
Boy's name. (5)
One who journeys. (9)
Place. (4)
Amuse. (9)
Volcano. (4)
Overcomes. (9)
Dwelling houses. (9)

Clues Across

Show places. (8)
Scottish town. (3)
Merry piece. (5)
Spanish lady. (6)
Unusual looking animals. (3-6)
Solidify. (3)

49

The Make You Very *Cross*-Words

Puzzle solvers are a happy lot.

The Make You Very *Cross*-Words 7.

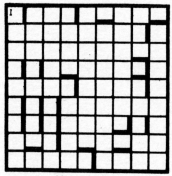

Costs. (8)
Contends. (4)
Stare. (4)
River of India. (5)
Seller. (6)
Old theatre of melodrama. (6)
Restrain. (5)
Roman poet. (4)

Clues Down
Rescued. (9)
Depend. (4)
Investigator. (8)
Lazy. (8)
Push. (5)
Baked item. (5, 4)
Inferred. (7)
Telling tales out of school. (8)
Employ. (3)
Sub-division of a cavalry regiment. (5)
Store of wealth. (8)

Clues Across
Expensive. (4)
Adroitness in personal relationships. (4)
Foot-travellers. (6)
Northern European. (9)
Make a mistake. (3)

The Make You Very *Cross*-Words 8.

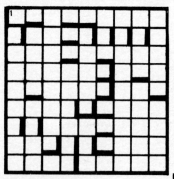

Express (3)   Hazard. (4)
Going back. (9)
Beam. (3)   Give way. (3)
Solitary. (4)
Most distant. (6)   Deer. (4)
African river. (7)

Clues Down.
Inquisitors. (9)
Premature. (8)
Portions left out. (9)
Chair. (4)   Chart. (3)
Scottish town. (4)
Hurry. (3)
Incurring defeat. (6)
Language not confined to verse. (5)
Girl's name. (4)
Enough. (4)
Canine. (5)
Lads. (4)

Clues Across
Main highway. (5, 4)
Sartorial expert. (6)
Arm or leg (4)
Bargain. (4)
Site for an artist. (5)

The Make You Very *Cross*-Words

Keep contented with Tim McKay's Puzzle Book.

The Make You Very *Cross*-Words 9.

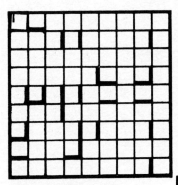

Clues Across

Shrub's ego (Anag.). (5-4)
Morning moisture. (3)
Money factory. (4)
Endured. (6)
Imitate. (3)
Countryside character. (5)

Indication. (5)
Rest. (9)
Friendly sign to acquaintance. (3)   Child's horse. (3)
Acting. (5)
Set of rules. (3)
Makes mistakes. (4)
Objector. (8)

Clues Down.

Dangers (Anag.). (7)
They travel from one country to another. (9)
Spanish peasant. (4)
Glittering decorations. (8)
Irish dish. (4)   Monster. (4)
Hold together. (4)
Mnemonics. (9)
Guarantee. (9)
Container. (4)
Proclaiming (9)
For the coin. (4)

The Make You Very *Cross*-Words 10.

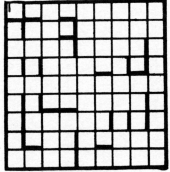

Clues Across

Tasty cuts of meat. (4, 5)
Camera part. (4)
South Wales peninsula. (5)
Declare. (3)
Knock lightly. (3)
Tear. (3, 2)
Foremen. (9)
Trials. (5)
Finished. (4)

Series of steps. (5)
Parliamentary body. (6)
Hunts out. (5)
Couch. (4)

Clues Down

Woollen garments. (9)
Look-out place on ship's mast. (5-4)
Shooting grounds. (6)
Watering place. (3)
Hurt. (4)
Bee's habitation. (4)
Unsullied. (4)
Clumsy man. (3)
You may have often signed yourself as an obedient one. (7)
Direction. (4)
Stare, poet (anag.). (9)
Send the money. (5)
The ladies have not yet married. (9)

Large Crosswords

ACROSS

1. Nice light? Hush, I'm member — but undecorated (7)
5. Hard finish when French lake goes to querulous start (7)
9. Old sailor is nearly a limited company (5)
10. They enable you to get a good grip (4-5)
11. It's usual — for us to be with Tom and Cary (9)
12. Elegance from learner in pighouse (5)
13. Give up — or go soft (5)
15. The QE1 and QE2 (9)
18. Things you get into — or take up (9)
19. Half full in the sky — not very gracious (5)
21. Label the French way to find a bilingual word (5)
23. Guardsman gets on the end of the train by swopping a letter (5, 3)
25. Con, Al, Viv and I prove we can have a jolly time together (9)
26. Is in the beer in church (5)
27. Greed all round me — and came out (7)
28. Tricks King caught in rivers noted for cattle, sands and salmon (7)

DOWN

1. Stiff outcome when a cart is upset and it's a shy outside (7)
2. Could be Sister, in short, in tent being stubborn (9)
3. Hurry along, fellow, with the tropical fruit (5)
4. Hears in the reed for practice (9)
5. In France the one greater part of the day is believed to be off Ilfracombe (5)
6. Mischarts to make a present day error (9)
7. University girl, by her outside (5)
8. The artist is her's for the bacon (7)
14. Little Diana in front of the ring isn't making up her mind (9)
16. Dine in disorder round a theatre seat (9)
17. Went on the box Vi deletes in a way (9)
18. The definite sort of word (7)
20. The Connecticut Connection (7)
22. Orgy for those about to begin (5)
23. City men, very proper, go golden about (5)
24. Slow speech from the doctor in front of the old bore (5)

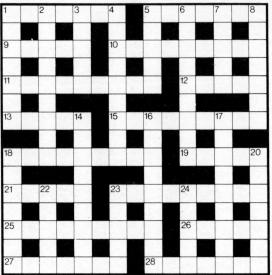

Almost 10,000 puzzles and Tim McKay still goes strong.

Large Crosswords

Large Crosswords 2.

ACROSS

1. Scent could be start of something grand in France (9)
6. Top doctor turns out a shirker (5)
9. Produced by heralds for poor little knights? (5, 4)
10. Eastern ruler has the beginning and end in jewellers (5)
12. Habit of the American era (5)
13. I get into the churches with political chiefs (9)
14. Capital — aim of most golfers (5)
16. Iron seats possibly made by someone with something to say (9)
19. Shun a longer word in service (9)
20. Getting the Saint into the dock could be like a lover's meeting (5)
21. The head of the place: very nearly a prince and I, with a pal (9)
23. A bit of a riot that ends up with spirit (5)
26. Battered in the kitchen (5)
27. Boastful types (9)
28. From The Oak came a commanding officer, Royal Navy (5)
29. They set a value on Ross asses arranged rather differently (9)

DOWN

2. Artists and politicians meet on the slopes (5)
3. Explosive force of Gentle G.I. when I come into the picture (9)
4. Distant, like a bit of leaf arranged not for close effect (4)
5. Do they take money for opening doors? (15)
7. You're on this side of the puzzle (7)
8. It's infamous! Not a cypher . . . Rio in front of us (9)
11. Ship that shapes a girl's eyes (5)
15. Arctic round a cart that has had an accident leaves you in the cold (9)
17. These renegades must, of course, save on their tailoring bills (9)
18. Nothing in the first part of the stick for the philosopher's follower (5)
22. Not ever in sane verse do you find it (5)
24. Say, it's not the sort of thing you can keep silent about (5)
25. Vague ending for a disorder (4)

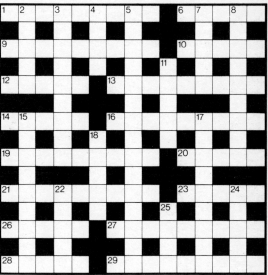

Shorten your bus or train journey with the Large crosswords.

Large Crosswords

ACROSS

1. Sent a poor sort of rep inside, grovelling (7)
5. Not so heavy as a coal barge (7)
9. Choose the best (5)
10. Fishy fruit? (5, 4)
11. Painter's colic (9)
12. Mistake by student at the east end of a church (5)
13. It's a wash out (6, 3)
16. Poet found in Irish tribe — handsome lot (5)
17. The lady could be Monsieur Adam (5)
19. Are they circular for round robins? (9)
22. The sort of mountains that encourage you to dance? (5)
23. Revolutionary exercise on the wagon (9)
25. How you go when you've just climbed your Everest? (2, 7)
26. Rub out age to the South East (5)
27. The other fellow's car is always, he says, this amount ahead (7)
28. Gets the better of the boys (7)

DOWN

1. Willowy Shakespearean type (7)
2. Music-makers from river side (5)
3. This could be the end (7)
4. Ring more than half an elephant in tone (9)
5. Left an emu, then right a different creature (5)
6. Members of this, like their weapons, are fired with enthusiasm (3, 4)
7. Often this is followed with two more and a hooray (9)
8. School could be a dear one (7)
14. Sign here (9)
15. Fictitious name — yet makes the whole farm shave (9)
17. Finding metal in Mars is strictly for the birds (7)
18. I'm matey — and here's the time in which to be that way (3, 4)
20. They're taken to court for having knowledge that others haven't got (7)
21. You and thousands who'd finish this (7)
23. Spends holiday writing a river postscript (5)
24. Eve gets a small ad. in — avoid her (5)

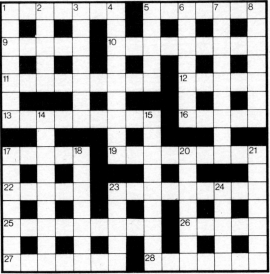

Keep up the crossword habit each day with the Daily Express.

Large Crosswords

ACROSS

1. Piteous petitions heard here (10, 5)
8. I got mixture eaten for bargain (9)
9. Declared to be a port on the Med (4)
11. Cues for songs about Poles (4)
17. Musical about a cooler? (7)
18. Childish noise or a quiet din (7)
19. Kind of grin — in Sussex? (3)
20. Some horses are debatable runners if they go off these (7)
21. Steer an Erse ant to the meanest anagram (7)
22. Anger that has not landed in the Emerald Isle (3)
23. Loving morning or nothing to us (7)
24. Drop of water (7)
25. Direction of the feast (4)
30. Romans never got this first in class (4)
31. Clever work I throttle with a vegetable (9)
32. Friendly people near your home show it (15)

DOWN

1. Tell off chap responsible for heating (5, 10)
2. Twice this and gentle was she (4)
3. Surgeon without issue (4)
4. Drinks for the little ones (4)
5. Ye are not quite finished but it's time (4)
6. The river, one hears, is scented (4)
7. They make a comforting alliteration on a winter afternoon (7, 8)
10. It hardly matters except that the pub goes to us eventually (9)
12. Profit motive of the master craftsman (2, 3, 4)
13. To which Arthurian holidaymakers returned many times? (7)
14. Reps sit askew — but keep on and on (7)
15. Incomplete contract perhaps or damaged toothpaste tube (4, 3)
16. Distant — or stand-offish (3, 4)
26. Taste that is partly small orange (4)
27. Bats could be made to wound (4)
28. Lace in the cruel sea (4)
29. Told to cook in drab oily rags (4)
30. Does a broad one have a Somerset accent? (4)

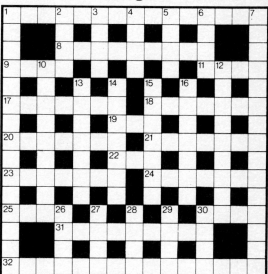

Don't commit suicide, the solutions are at the back of the book.

Large Crosswords

ACROSS
1. Sausages among old cars? (7)
5. Makes a delivery in satirical fashion (5, 2)
9. Doctor gets round the outsize bird by making an objection (5)
10. Cash isn't safe when he is about (9)
11. Betting man may have summed them up (4)
12. Many a price-rise is a bit (5)
13. Book of deeds (4)
16. Up the creek maybe (5)
18. Necessary having a bad tail to the German city (9)
20. A torn page for someone trying to give help (9)
23. Wallace the film star not to be sniffed at (5)
25. No taboo at this Scots resort (4)
26. Cover that entrance! (5)
27. Ready for anything, having won that one (4)
31. All aboard (9)
32. Chase the four-legged brute (5)
33. Lazy types you could find by analysing the red dogs (7)
34. Win 200 in leather (7)

DOWN
1. Best around the pod in a way (3, 4)
2. Quite sane wanderer (5)
3. Title-holder with yearly contents (4)
4. Spectre might do the twist (7)
5. Becomes a landlord on his own (7)
6. Not a well-remembered type of German (4)
7. Being choosy about Clive's tee (9)
8. Pal about oars makes a kind of umbrella (7)
14. Pools make a return for the ship (5)
15. Shoemakers, over-proud, too (5)
17. Took from the value; item of literature indeed (9)
19. Droop, alas, a great deal holds answer (3)
20. Go where deep runs back, enclosing endless rock (7)
21. Spring as about harvests (7)
22. Foreign coins in Lupescu dosshouses (7)
24. Dee idly provides anagram mixture. Gave up (7)
28. Entertained — timed before noon (5)
29. Fast worker alongside Burke (4)
30. Neat part of touch I can read of in fashion pages (4)

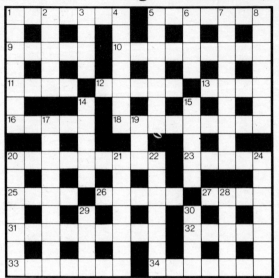

Look out for further puzzle books by Tim McKay.

Personality Codewords No. 1.

1=0; 2=N; 3=S; 4=T; 5=L; 6=A; 7=I; 8=D; 9=E; 10=M; 11=C; 12=F; 13=U; 14=R; 15=V; 16=B; 17=K; 18=G; 19=H; 20=P. The personality: VAL Doonican.

Personality Codewords No. 2.

1=X; 2=W; 3=I; 4=O; 5=F; 6=A; 7=L; 8=S; 9=E; 10=V; 11=R; 12=P; 13=C; 14=D; 15=N; 16=G; 17=T; 18=H; 19=U; 20=B. The personality: CILLA Black.

Personality Codewords No. 3.

1=U; 2=O; 3=A; 4=T; 5=S; 6=E; 7=R; 8=L; 9=I; 10=P; 11=N; 12=F; 13=C; 14=D; 15=B; 16=K; 17=M; 18=H; 19=G; 20=Y. The personality: LARRY Grayson.

Personality Codewords No. 4.

1=D; 2=L; 3=A; 4=S; 5=W; 6=O; 7=I; 8=N; 9=E; 10=R; 11=K; 12=G; 13=C; 14=T; 15=M; 16=B; 17=U; 18=H; 19=F; 20=Y; 21=X; 22=P; 23=V. The personality: ROLF Harris.

Personality Codewords No. 5.

1=L; 2=O; 3=S; 4=E; 5=N; 6=I; 7=A; 8=B; 9=R; 10=M; 11=D; 12=C; 13=H; 14=T; 15=U; 16=F; 17=W; 18=V; 19=P; 20=G; 21=Z. The personality: ROGER Moore.

Personality Codewords No. 6.

1=C; 2=A; 3=R; 4=T; 5=E; 6=N; 7=M; 8=I; 9=O; 10=F; 11=L; 12=D; 13=V; 14=B; 15=S; 16=P; 17=H; 18=U; 19=K; 20=G; 21=W; 22=Y. The personality: President CARTER.

Personality Codewords No. 7.

1=B; 2=A; 3=L; 4=E; 5=S; 6=O; 7=D; 8=N; 9=I; 10=C; 11=T; 12=P; 13=R; 14=H; 15=G; 16=M; 17=W; 18=U; 19=Y; 20=V. The personality: Sophia LOREN.

SOLUTIONS

Codewords No. 1.
1=Q; 2=K; 3=S; 4=A;
5=E; 6=R; 7=T; 8=I; 9=O;
10=L; 11=P; 12=C; 13=U;
14=B; 15=M; 16=N;
17=V; 18=G; 19=D;
20=Y; 21=F; 22=H.

Codewords No. 2.
1=O; 2=S; 3=V; 4=E;
5=L; 6=A; 7=T; 8=I;
9=N; 10=M; 11=U; 12=Y;
13=F; 14=B; 15=G; 16=C;
17=R; 18=D; 19=H; 20=P;
21=W.

Codewords No. 3.
1=R; 2=I; 3=D; 4=O;
5=A; 6=S; 7=T; 8=C;
9=E; 10=P; 11=G; 12=M;
13=U; 14=B; 15=L; 16=N;
17=X; 18=H.

Codewords No. 4.
1=R; 2=T; 3=O; 4=N;
5=D; 6=A; 7=S; 8=H;
9=I; 10=W; 11=G; 12=K;
13=U; 14=C; 15=E; 16=X;
17=P; 18=L; 19=M; 20=F;
21=V; 22=B.

Sunshine Puzzles No. 1.

ACROSS: Aniseed. Towpath. Biped. Monstrous. Telephony. Regal. Stiff. Privateer. Annulment. Lupin. Ennui. Paregoric. Tentative. Lucre. Deepens. Toddler.
DOWN: Arbutus. Impulsion. End up. Damson pie. Tinny. Waterfall. Among. Hustler. Fulminate. Interment. Empirical. Alerted. Nuclear. Nonce. Plies. Gelid.

Sunshine Puzzles No. 2.

ACROSS: Ratebooks. Crime. Startling. Islam. Grape. Fortunate. Locum. Attracted. Interpret. State. Empirical. Scowl. Sneak. Atrocious. Ashen. Hermitage.
DOWN: Aster. Enrapture. Ogle. King of the castle. Resin. Mean theft. Stork. Ornaments. Catechist. Split. Irate. Wrung. Form.

Sunshine Puzzles No. 3.

ACROSS: Entails. Tactics. Crisp. Political. Regularly. Plum. Different. Whilst. Dared. Equipment. Paste. Decadence. Oversight. Larks. Elderly. Dusters.
DOWN: Encored. Thing. Impulse. Supersede. Tally. Catspaw. Inclusive. Salient. Farmstead. Truncated. Deplore. Dresser. Puddles. Tresses. Doggy. Nerve.

Sunshine Puzzles No. 4.

ACROSS: At the drop of a hat. Propagate. Ours. Also. Implore. Hairnet. Ace. Gherkin. Riposte. Eli. Avenger. Soprano. Hats. Seen. Condiment. Swordswallowing.
DOWN: Auto-biographies. Hips. Door. Opal. Area. Top of the morning. Represent. Landscape. Corkage. Deanery. Cherish. Oilpipe. Scar. Inks. Mica. Bell. Stew.

Sunshine Puzzles No. 5.

ACROSS: Village. Assault. Level. Objection. Nark. Fiend. Here. Ennui. Motorists. Magnitude. Salad. Rate. Nippy. Plea. Coalition. Curio. Elevate. Earthen.
DOWN: Valance. Lover. Able. Egotism. Adjunct. Sack. Universal. Tunnels. Tryst. Digit. Nightmare. Old. Miracle. Utilise. Expanse. Dragoon. Lurch. Pisa. Scar.

Sunshine Puzzles No. 6.

ACROSS: Lord Chancellor. Vodka. Chorister. Ironmoulds. Gala. Imminent. Famish. Latest. Cashmere. Null. Condiments. Situation. Eerie. Precociousness.
DOWN: Love-in-idleness. Rodeo. Clamminess. Accruing. Cloudy. Laid. Ostracise. Breathlessness. Fathomless. Mutilator. Fandango. Zodiac. Nerve. Talc.

Sunshine Puzzles No. 7.

ACROSS: Greyness. Waster. Scotched. Abound. Emigrated. Ledge. Ida. Accept. Nurse. Ember. Garden. Pea. Ernie. Graduates. Spouts. Seashore. Desire. Stutters.
DOWN: Gusted. Exotic. Nicer. Sweet. Ambulance. Thunders. Redeemed. Editor. Arc. Carpenter. Engage. Released. Abandons. Dad. Stroke. Asters. Adept. Upset.

Sunshine Puzzles No. 8.

ACROSS: Lard. Conductor. Ramp. Descendant. Cultures. Stream. Investigations. Disconsolately. Robust. Samovars. Silver coin. Skid. Remainder. Arcs.
DOWN: Lyrics. Rumblings. Operettas. Duck. Constitution. Ovate. Atomise. Queen of Sheba. Galvanise. Oil tanker. Address. Asides. Bilge. Scan.

Sunshine Puzzles No. 9.

ACROSS: Secretary. Audit. Attic. Cauterise. Inexact. Giggles. Three score. Abel. Call Achromatic. Lap-dogs. Foghorn. Sovereign. Abhor. Mitre. Red-headed.
DOWN: Statistical. Cathedral. Enchased. Ascetic. Younger. Avenge. Drill Toe. Self-centred. Betrothed. Emigrate. Cashier. Refined. Course. Pivot. Sum.

Sunshine Puzzles No. 10.

ACROSS: Jack of all trades. Mangler. Trollop. Opera. See. Inter. Tar. Basket. Prison. Image. Exotic. Gentle. She. Kedge. Pen. Vexed. Aviator. Bullion. The Daily Express.
DOWN: Jam for breakfast. Canners. Oil-cake. Arrest. Latter. Roomier. Dilutes. Superintendants. Earache. Tic. Peg. On-drive. Inertia. Envelop. Textile. Spiral. Enable.

SOLUTIONS

Monkey Puzzles No. 1.

ACROSS: 1 Encores. 5 Emperor. 9 Tempo. 10 Apparatus. 11 Blasted. 12 Overdue. 13 Spy. 15 Elders. 17 Asters. 19 Inner. 20 Strewn. 22 Tested. 25 Hew. 27 Pastime. 29 Embargo. 30 Irritated. 31 Olive. 32 Timbers. 33 Relents.
DOWN: 1 Eatable. 2 Commander. 3 Rooster. 4 Shards. 5 Employ. 6 Parleys. 7 Rated. 8 Russets. 14 Pence. 16 Sin. 17 Art. 18 Extortion. 20 Sophist. 21 Whistle. 23 Embroil. 24 Drovers. 25 Heaths. 26 Welder. 28 Strum.

Monkey Puzzles No. 2.

ACROSS: 1 Pleasure. 5 Basset. 9 Inventive. 11 Enrol. 12 Opera. 13 Wits. 14 Scar. 16 Obey. 17 Respect. 20 Tat. 21 Dresser. 22 Axis. 25 Nail. 26 Scan. 27 Inter. 29 Ideas. 30 Scenarios. 31 Sitter. 32 Stresses.
DOWN: 1 Prison. 2 Envies. 3 Sunday best. 4 Railway tracks. 6 Apes. 7 Stricken. 8 Tolerate. 10 Entertainment. 15 Assimilate. 18 Adenoids. 19 Resident. 23 Strips. 24 Trysts. 28 Isle.

Monkey Puzzles No. 3.

ACROSS: 1 Action. 5 Wiser. 9 Era. 11 Remnant. 12 The Pair. 13 Wee. 14 Trapeze. 15 Rocking. 16 Rusty. 18 Gentleman. 21 Automatic. 24 Regal. 26 Unaware. 28 Nodular. 29 Lot. 30 Applied. 31 Elastic. 32 Ems. 33 Eager. 34 Throng.

DOWN: 2 Compass. 3 Imagery. 4 Net weight. 5 Water. 6 Stencil. 7 Realism. 8 Preternatural. 10 Original price. 17 Too. 19 No contest. 20 Eve. 22 Trample. 23 Meaning. 24 Red hair. 25 Gelatin. 27 Elder.

Monkey Puzzles No. 4.

ACROSS: 6 Entertainments. 9 Sour. 10 Fluff. 11 Lord. 12 Impudent. 13 Lotion. 14 Nested. 16 Admits. 19 Gallop. 21 Pleasure. 23 Miss. 24 Alert. 25 Rack. 26 Indecipherable.
DOWN: 1 Recommendation. 2 Sternums. 3 Trifle. 4 Snuffled. 5 Pellet. 7 Acuity. 8 Terror-stricken. 15 Emphatic. 17 Inscribe. 18 Speech. 20 Lashed. 22 Entire.

Monkey Puzzles No. 5.

ACROSS: 1 Scientologist. 9 Hyena. 10 Pink. 11 Sloe. 13 Last scene. 14 Recap. 15 Stands. 17 Lonesome. 19 Succeeds. 21 Poison. 24 Plump. 25 Exonerate. 27 Eats. 28 Aida. 29 React. 30 Adding-machine.
DOWN: 2 Chess. 3 Elapsed. 4 Topper. 5 Lancelot. 6 Salacious. 7 The Last Supper. 8 People in tents. 12 Brie. 16 Accounted. 18 Adhering. 20 Espy. 22 On earth. 23 Sonata. 26 Again.

SOLUTIONS

Monkey Puzzles No. 6.

ACROSS: 1 Court hearing. 10 Despair. 12 Servant. 13 Cad. 14 Vie. 15 Erudite. 16 Seafire. 17 Teeny. 19 Transient. 22 Shattered. 25 Refer. 27 Matures. 29 Expound. 31 Cos. 32 Eft. 33 Nirvana. 34 Scatter. 35 Short measure.

DOWN: 2 Obscure. 3 Readily. 4 Harvester. 5 Asses. 6 Inroads. 7 Granite. 8 Advertisement. 9 Street traders. 11 Pad. 18 Nut. 20 Addressee. 21 Ire. 23 Attires. 24 Tornado. 25 Repeals. 26 Flutter. 28 Scant. 30 Oft.

Monkey Puzzles No. 7.

ACROSS: 1 Progressionist. 9 Argued. 10 Anathema. 12 Amending. 13 Scolds. 14 Lily. 15 Endear. 19 Fondle. 20 Grid. 23 Grooms. 24 Emulsion. 26 Abortive. 27 Cinema. 28 Speechlessness.

DOWN: 2 Ruggedly. 3 Greedy. 4 Song. 5 Optician. 6 Ideals. 7 Transcendental. 8 Parallelograms. 11 Indeed. 16 Dreams. 17 Dogmatic. 18 Trailers. 21 Jocose. 22 Albion. 25 Evil.

Monkey Puzzles No. 8.

ACROSS: 7 Clamour. 8 Proverb. 10 Our. 11 Marital. 12 Asphalt. 13 Extra. 15 Fanatical. 17 Oaf. 19 Recount. 21 Yes. 22 Afterward. 24 Rumba. 26 Imprint. 28 Remoter. 30 Oil. 31 Neither. 32 Attired.

DOWN: 1 Parrot. 2 Cost. 3 Prolific. 4 Sprain. 5 Competitor. 6 Beta. 7 Commemoration. 9 Battle-scarred. 14 Air Freight. 16 Coy. 18 Fat. 20 Underlay. 23 Actors. 24 Mature. 27 Pain. 29 Mite.

Monkey Puzzles No. 9.

ACROSS: 1 Famished. 5 Gasped. 9 Intercept. 12 Isles. 13 Taste. 14 Pretences. 15 Unadvertised. 19 Christenings. 21 Telephone. 23 Upset. 25 Ricks. 26 Situation. 28 Resist. 29 Expended.

DOWN: 1 Flinty. 2 Motes. 3 Surrender. 4 Dip. 6 Alike. 7 Police dog. 8 Disaster. 10 Expressions. 11 Theatre seat. 16 Necklaces. 17 Stipulate. 18 Barterer. 20 Atoned. 22 Pests. 24 Spied. 27 Ire.

Monkey Puzzles No. 10.

ACROSS: 1 Slap down. 4 Blocks. 9 Envisages. 11 Rouse. 12 Value. 13 Overacted. 14 Consequences. 18 Tesselations. 20 Scarlatti. 22 These. 24 Altar. 25 Ownership. 26 Eldest. 27 Preserve.

DOWN: 1 Swerve. 2 Anvil. 3 Dispenses. 5 Larva. 6 Courtesan. 7 Speedhog. 8 Asseveration. 10 Good question. 15 Outlasted. 16 Chilterns. 17 Dissuade. 19 Temple. 21 Lyres. 23 Ether.

SOLUTIONS

Large Crosswords No. 1.

ACROSS: 1 Shimmer. 5 Lacquer. 9 Anson. 10 Hand-rails. 11 Customary. 12 Style. 13 Yield. 15 Shipmates. 18 Attitudes. 19 Sulky. 21 Table. 23 Guards van. 25 Convivial. 26 Aisle. 27 Emerged. 28 Deludes. DOWN: 1 Starchy. 2 Insistent. 3 Mango. 4 Rehearsed. 5 Lundy. 6 Christmas. 7 Unity. 8 Rashers. 14 Dithering. 16 Installed. 17 Televised. 18 Article. 20 Yankees. 22 Binge. 23 Guild. 24 Drawl.

Large Crosswords No. 2.

ACROSS: 1 Fragrance. 6 Drone. 9 Small arms. 10 Agate. 12 Usage. 13 Ministers. 14 Paris. 16 Assertion. 19 Attention. 20 Tryst. 21 Principal. 23 Scrum. 26 Stove. 27 Braggarts. 28 Acorn. 29 Assessors. DOWN: 2 Ramps. 3 Gelignite. 4 Afar. 5 Commissionaires. 7 Right. 8 Notorious. 11 Liner. 15 Antarctic. 17 Turncoats. 18 Stoic. 22 Never. 24 Utter. 25 Ague.

Large Crosswords No. 3.

ACROSS: 1 Serpent. 5 Lighter. 9 Elect. 10 Lemon sole. 11 Distemper. 12 Lapse. 13 Rained off. 16 Behan. 17 Madam. 19 Envelopes. 22 Rocky. 23 Cartwheel. 25 In triumph. 26 Erase. 27 Streets. 28 Masters.

DOWN: 1 Slender. 2 Reeds. 3 Extreme. 4 Telephone. 5 Lemur. 6 Gun Club. 7 Troopship. 8 Roedean. 14 Indicator. 15 Faversham. 17 Martins. 18 May-time. 20 Lawyers. 21 Solvers. 23 Camps. 24 Evade.

Large Crosswords No. 4.

ACROSS: 1 Bankruptcy Court. 8 Negotiate. 9 Said. 11 Rods. 17 Fanfare. 18 Prattle. 19 Rye. 20 Rockers. 21 Nearest. 22 Ire. 23 Amorous. 24 Niagara. 25 East. 30 Beta. 31 Artichoke. 32 Neighbourliness. DOWN: 1 Blast-furnaceman. 2 Kind. 3 Urge. 4 Tots. 5 Year. 6 Oder. 7 Toasted teacakes. 10 Innocuous. 12 On the make. 13 Camelot. 14 Persist. 15 Open end. 16 Far-away. 26 Tang. 27 Stab. 28 Ecru. 29 Boil. 30 Bean.

Large Crosswords No. 5.

ACROSS: 1 Bangers. 5 Sends up. 9 Demur. 10 Embezzler. 11 Odds. 12 Steep. 13 Acts. 16 Tidal. 18 Essential. 20 Patronage. 23 Beery. 25 Oban. 26 Porch. 27 Game. 31 Entrained. 32 Hound. 33 Dodgers. 34 Succeed. DOWN: 1 Bed post. 2 Nomad. 3 Earl. 4 Sceptre. 5 Sublets. 6 Nazi. 7 Selective. 8 Parasol. 14 Sloop. 15 Snobs. 17 Detracted. 19 Sag. 20 Proceed. 21 Abounds. 22 Escudos. 24 Yielded. 28 Amuse. 29 Hare. 30 Chic.

SOLUTIONS

A dip into TIM McKAY'S Postbag . . .

THERE must be hundreds of people who, like me, look forward to their daily ration of 'puzzling' and I would like to pass on our thanks to Tim for all his efforts on our behalf. It can't be easy setting puzzles each and every day of publication . . . but keep up the good work!

(Mrs) K Sizer, St Mary's Road, Benfleet, Essex.

TIM McKAY is king of all! Good health to him!

(Miss) C. M. Browne, Devonshire Road, Blackpool.

THE Small Crossword . . . the first thing I read when I receive the newspaper. All my good wishes.

(Mr) G Russell, Herne Bay, Kent.

YOUR small Crossword daily is a delight.

(Mrs) B. D. Poole, Tilgate, Sussex.

MAY I thank Tim McKay for the excellent crosswords? The humour of some of the anagrams is comparable only to Giles's cartoons. I have often thought that Tim and Giles are the same person, or at least related to each other.

(Mr) Joseph McKiernon, Shannon Rd, Birmingham.

I ALWAYS do your crossword after cleaning the grate and doing the fire. Not often I am stumped. Best wishes.

(Mrs) E Webb, (84 Years young), Skirlaugh, Humberside.

And now a warning . . .

IT IS my intention to write a television play that includes a character who is a crossword compiler . . .

(Mr) K. J. Squires, Hamworthy, Poole, Dorset.

and a P.S. from TIM...

I get a big thrill on opening readers' letters from all over the world and I spend a lot of time answering them. But please don't send me money for copies of Tim McKay's Puzzle Book No. 1 or Crosswords Galore No. 9. Send these remittances straight to Express Books, 121 Fleet Street, London EC4P 4JT. And look out for Tim McKay's Puzzle Book No. 2. It won't be long now.